W

This book describes the various welding processes and procedures, and discusses their uses for production and repair work. Intended primarily for the welder and the welding student, it is hoped that it will provide a knowledge of the factors that influence the quality of welding and an appreciation of the limitations of the different processes available with regard to their economical and efficient application. As the welding engineer will have to be familiar with both Imperial and metric units for some years to come, the values of quantities are given in Imperial units with their SI (Système Internationale) equivalents indicated in brackets afterwards. The text is fully illustrated.

This book is unusually well indexed and cross referenced. Therefore readers seeking information on specific aspects of welding are recommended to use the contents lists (pages vii to x) and/or the index (pages 177 to 180) for quick reference.

TEACH YOURSELF BOOKS

WELDING

C. G. Bainbridge

TEACH YOURSELF BOOKS
Hodder and Stoughton

First printed 1962
Fourth edition 1980
Fourth impression 1984

Copyright © 1962, 1973, 1977, 1980
Hodder and Stoughton Ltd.

ISBN 0 340 25956 6

Printed in Great Britain for
Hodder and Stoughton Educational,
a division of Hodder and Stoughton Ltd,
Mill Road, Dunton Green, Sevenoaks, Kent,
by Richard Clay (The Chaucer Press) Ltd,
Bungay, Suffolk

Foreword

In preparing this book originally, the author intended it for the welding novice, the engineering student and apprentice, or the draughtsman – to review in simple terms the various welding processes then available and their applications; one of the objectives was to indicate the advantages of welding in its application to both production and repair work. However, in ten years or so, the welding scene has altered considerably and much revision to the original text has been necessary. There is, perhaps, little need in these days to extol the advantages of welding as a joining process, since it is more or less generally accepted that where pieces of metal have to be joined welding in some form will be used. While the old 'basic' processes – oxy-acetylene and arc welding, and spot welding – are still widely used, the technology of welding becomes ever more complex, due to the introduction of new metals, applications, processes and equipment. It is therefore necessary to choose carefully the type of process, the procedure or the electrode to be used in order to realise fully the potential advantages of welding.

Moreover, since the book was originally prepared, several processes and applications have died out completely, either because the need has gone or because newer metals and processes have changed the application; deletions have been made accordingly. The list of relevant British Standards publications has also been completely revised and brought up to date to include the latest additions.

Since the author finds that the book is largely bought by practical welders and welding students, he hopes that the information it contains will enable them to acquire the 'background' knowledge necessary to understand the

function of the various processes and procedures, to
know something of those factors that influence the quality of welding and to appreciate the limitations of the
various processes available with regard to their economical and efficient application.

Contents

Part 1: Welding Processes

Part 2: Welding for Manufacture

List of Tables

Acknowledgements

The author is very grateful to Mr. Jack Peach for his help in metricating the text of this new edition.

His thanks are also due to 'Machinery Lloyd' for permission to use their drawings for Figs. 48 to 51; to Messrs. Iliffe & Sons Ltd. for permission to use material from the author's *Gas Welding and Cutting* for Fig. 55; and to Temple Press Ltd. for permission to use sundry information from the author's *Welding Repairs*.

A number of revisions have been made to this edition as the result of suggestions from metal manufacturers and others to whom the author is extremely grateful for their co-operation and interest.

Note on Metrication

For some years to come it will be necessary for engineers to be familiar with both Imperial and metric units. In this book values of quantities are given in Imperial units, followed by the metric equivalent. The change to metric units is being taken as an opportunity to rationalise practice. It follows, therefore, that in some cases the commonly used metric value will not be a direct equivalent of the Imperial. Where future metric practice can be assumed, this rational value is given instead of an exact conversion.

Direct conversions to a practical accuracy are shown in brackets thus ( ).

Likely metric preferred practical values are given in square brackets thus [ ].

A list of common metric equivalents is given in the Appendix.

Part I

Welding Processes

The tremendous development of various welding processes has revolutionised the design and manufacture of almost all metal products; welded joints have superseded other methods of jointing, and welded assemblies have displaced castings, forgings and other types of construction in many industries. Welding has also extended the use of metals in all phases of industrial development and has facilitated the introduction of some metals into new or unusual applications, e.g. the use of aluminium alloys in shipbuilding and for piping, bridges and other structures.

This progress has entailed the expenditure of a vast amount of time and money in development by manufacturers of welding equipment, weldable metals and welded metal products, and in research and testing covering all aspects of welding, to ensure the maximum safety, strength and reliability of the welding joint in all its applications. Industrial and national research, advisory and standardisation bodies have also been set up to establish reliable procedures and standards, and to interchange welding information throughout the world; moreover, a new class of professional engineer has now been evolved – the Welding Engineer.

The Advantages of Welding

Reviewing briefly some of the more common applications of welding, we find that in the heavy industries welding has almost entirely superseded riveting in the construction of buildings, bridges, ships, pressure vessels, tanks, gas holders and many other types of steel work. Moreover, welding is not just another type of joint – its use generally improves the product. For example, a welded ship costs less to build and is up to 10% lighter than a riveted ship due to the elimination of rivet heads and plate overlaps, and to the use of light alloys; maintenance and running costs are also lower.

Railways

Similar advantages are realised in other types of welded structures. Welded all-metal railway vehicles are lighter, stronger, and more fire- and damage-resisting than those using other types of construction; the efficiency of the modern diesel electric locomotive is greatly dependent on welding, which is used extensively for the chassis, engine and body construction.

On the permanent way, the welded rail joint eliminates noise – especially in underground systems – and reduces wear and tear on rolling stock; in addition, it eliminates battered rail ends and loose joints which normally necessitate constant track maintenance. Railways are also extensive users of various welding processes for repair and maintenance work, saving many thousands of pounds annually in prolonging the life and maintaining the safety of crossings, switches, bridges, locomotives and other rolling stock.

Motor Cars and Aircraft

In the field of road transport, modern road vehicles utilise a considerable amount of welding (of various types) for chassis, wheels and body construction, and for the assembly of pressed steel components. Welding has also always been closely associated with the development of the aircraft industry, and the modern aeroplane is particularly dependent on welding for the production and servicing of the sheet metal fuselage and heat-resisting jet engine components involved in its construction. Incidentally, the conquest of space owes much to the weldability of the metals employed for engine and space craft construction.

Pipelines

Our industrial and domestic requirements of gas, water and oil are very largely supplied by pipelines, and our buildings are heated and cooled by piped air or water. For all kinds of pipework, welding can provide joints that are less expensive, lighter, smoother, more reliable and need less maintenance than other types of joints. Moreover, welded joints occupy the minimum of space – an important factor in the compact arrangement of service piping in ships, factories and other buildings. In atomic power plants, oil rigs and refineries, welding is used extensively for joints in pressure vessels, heat exchangers, and piping in alloy steels and other special alloys.

Chemicals and Food

In the brewing, chemical, paper and food industries, welding is invaluable for providing smooth, easily cleaned and corrosion-resisting joints in the non-ferrous and corrosion-resisting metals that are largely employed.

Displacing Castings

For many engineering productions, castings and forgings have been replaced by welded steel fabrications, which are lighter and stronger, less expensive, need less machining and can be produced with the usual facilities of a steelwork fabrication shop. Machinery with welded parts can often be run at higher speeds than machinery with cast parts and requires less power; lighter and stronger welded construction reduces freight costs and floor loads, and minimises risk of breakage in transit.

Preventing Wear

An entirely different type of welding application is the deposition of wear-resisting metals, enabling parts that are subjected to severe wear in service to be made of comparatively inexpensive and easily fabricated metals, and yet have excellent wearing properties with wear-resisting metal deposited on wearing surfaces and edges. The tremendous use of earth-moving, materials-handling, well-drilling, dredging and mining equipment involves very considerable wear problems which have stimulated the introduction of a wide variety of hard-facing and wear-resisting depositing metals to suit almost every wear-resisting requirement (see page 131).

Repair and Maintenance

The repair and maintenance of metal parts and engineering equipment generally has been simplified by welding, which enables broken and worn parts to be quickly repaired, very often at a fraction of the cost of a new replacement; foundries also make extensive use of welding for the reclamation of defective castings. Metals can be welded and cut under water, thus greatly improving the resources of oil rig and dock and harbour builders and repairers, enabling underwater pipelines to be installed or repaired and facilitating marine salvage work.

Basic Principles of Welding

For many years the term 'welding'* – as used by blacksmiths and other iron workers – referred to a lapped or scarfed joint (see Fig. 1) between mild steel or wrought iron bars, which were heated in a forge fire and then hammered into close contact. The efficiency and strength of the joint depended entirely on the correct temperature of the joint surfaces and the right amount of hammering

* Also called 'fire welding' or 'forge welding'.

applied. The production of a sound, reliable weld of this type necessitated considerable experience and skill on the part of the blacksmith. To melt or overheat the joint surfaces would render the metal liable to atmospheric oxidation or 'burning' in the fire. On the other hand, if the metal was not heated enough, the surfaces would not be sufficiently plastic to bond together.

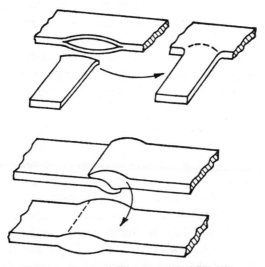

Fig. 1. Typical Blacksmiths' Welds.

The hammering also had to be skilfully applied, since excessively heavy blows displaced the metal too much and, if carried on too long after the metal had cooled, adhesion, not a weld, would be the result.

A later development enabled steel plates to be lap welded for the manufacture of cylindrical vessels and pipes – the plate edges were heated with suitable water gas flames to the required temperature, after which the joint surfaces were pressed together by means of rollers above and below the joint; similarly, rolled butt-jointed pipe could be welded by heating the joint edges and pressing them together by drawing the pipe through a die.

However, the blacksmith's weld, which is a non-fusion pressure weld, is suitable only for joining low carbon steel and wrought iron bars, and it will be appreciated that it was very limited in its application to the manufacture of metal products; it has now been almost entirely superseded by the arc, gas fusion and resistance welding processes that are the subject of this book.

As shown in Fig. 2, there are a considerable number of welding processes. Most of them involve fusion of the

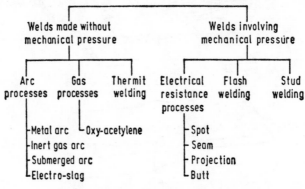

Fig. 2. Fusion Welding Processes.

joining edges or surfaces, but for ease of reference they are divided into two categories: those that involve only fusion without mechanical pressure, as in arc and gas welding, and those that involve the application of mechanical pressure to the fused surfaces, as in spot and flash welding.

Fusion welds made without mechanical pressure

With the non-pressure processes, the joint edges or surfaces are melted by the highly localised heat of an electric arc or gas flame; this is fusion welding, and it is applicable to almost any type of joint in any thickness used for the manufacture and repair of metal products.

Metal may also be deposited for rebuilding worn parts or providing wear-resisting surfaces and, whereas the original forge welding process was applicable only to iron or mild steel, fusion welding can be used for both ferrous and non-ferrous metals.

With some types of sheet metal joint, the joint edges are merely melted together to complete the joint (see Fig. 3). Generally, however, it is necessary to melt in

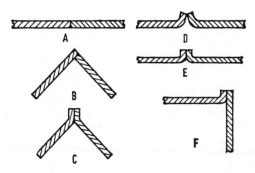

Fig. 3. Typical Edge Joints for Sheet Metals.

(Except for A – not suitable for gas or arc welding nickel alloys or aluminium.)

some additional filler metal to compensate for any gap between the joint edges and to provide a small amount of reinforcement to the joint. On thick metal, the joint edges are usually chamfered to ensure fusion throughout the full thickness of the joint (see Fig. 4).

In metal arc welding, filler metal is melted from the end of the electrode; in gas flame, carbon arc and tungsten arc welding, it is supplied from a separate feed wire or rod. Actually, it is usually an advantage to add filler metal because its composition can be arranged to provide strengthening, deoxidising and fluxing ingredients which improve the quality of the weld and make welding easier, especially for metals that tend to change their characteristics when heated or melted.

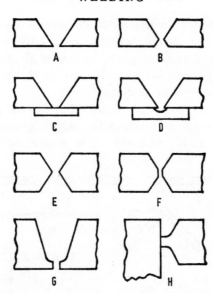

Fig. 4. Butt Joint Edge Preparations for Thick Metal.

A: For gas welding. 60°–70° vee (over ⅛ in [3 mm] thick).
B: For arc welding. Sharp corners at bottom of vee removed.
C: Backing strip joint for arc welding tank bottoms and pipe joints where back of joint is inaccessible. Backing strip welds to bottom of vee. D: Thick grooved copper backing strip under joint to control penetration; for steel and non-ferrous metals. Backing strip removed after welding. E: For vertical two-operator gas or inert arc welding (used for copper and aluminium), or for arc welding if both sides accessible. F: For arc welding in vertical position where both sides equally accessible. G: For thick plates; uses slightly less weld metal than vee joints. H: For arc welding where only one component can be prepared, e.g. flanges onto pipes or vessels.

Protecting the Molten Metal
It is most important to protect the molten weld metal from contact with the atmosphere in order to avoid the formation of nitrides and oxides, which may weaken the joint and alter the character of the weld metal.

With coated electrode arc welding, the burning of the coating produces gases which envelope the metal globules in their passage from the core wire to the job; some of the coating also melts and provides slag to cover the weld metal, as shown diagrammatically in Fig. 5, A.

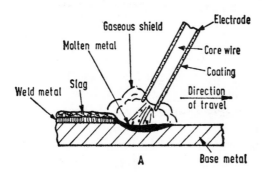

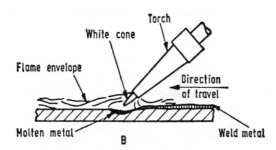

Fig. 5. Manual Welding.
A: Arc welding. B: Oxy-acetylene welding (see also Fig. 7, page 14).

With gas welding, some protection is afforded by the second combustion stage of the flame which covers the weld zone, as shown in Fig. 5, B. This, however, is not enough for many non-ferrous metals that oxidise very readily; therefore, for most metals, except steel, a flux is used to provide a slag covering for the weld pool. The flux slag protection of the molten metal is, of course, applicable only to the surface of the metal and does not include the underside of the joint, which, at the point of penetration, is also molten. Hence, for some metals (e.g. stainless steels) it is desirable to apply flux to the underside of the joint edges in order to prevent oxidation. The weld metal protection afforded by these processes is, however, only partially effective, and the more recently developed arc processes tend to provide more positive protection of the weld surface. In the submerged arc process a flux powder completely covers the weld zone, and in the electro-slag process the molten metal is covered completely by molten slag; these processes are described later.

In inert gas arc welding, the surface of the weld is most efficiently protected by the inert gas fed through the torch, and underside protection may also be provided by passing some of the same gas through a suitable channel under the joint, or through the pipe when this process is used for making pipe joints.

Fuel gas	Approx. calorific value		Flame temperature °C	
	Btu/ft³	MJ/m³	With oxygen	With air
Acetylene	1450–1550	54–58	3100–3500	2200–2400
Butane	3000–3400	112–127	3000	2000
Propane	2300–2400	86–90	2700	2100
Hydrogen	280–340	10·4–12·7	2300–2700	2000

Table 1. Calorific Values and Temperatures of Flames with Various Fuel Gases.

Gas Fusion Welding

The only satisfactory combination of gases for gas welding is oxygen and acetylene; oxygen is, of course, always necessary in order to obtain the maximum heat value from any fuel gas employed. Compared with propane or hydrogen, acetylene provides the hottest flame, the greatest concentration of heat, the most economical gas combination and an inert gas envelope, or waste flame (see Fig. 6).

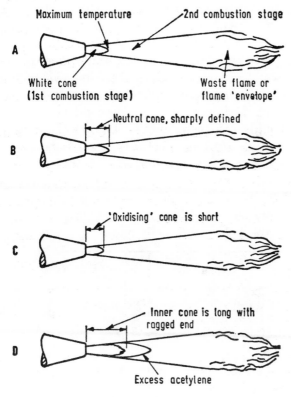

Fig. 6. The Oxy-acetylene Flame.

A: 1st combustion stage (white cone): oxygen and acetylene burn. 2nd combustion stage: carbon monoxide and hydrogen produced by 1st stage burn with oxygen from surrounding air. Flame envelope consists of carbon dioxide and water vapour from 2nd stage.

B, C & D: The three types of adjustment.

The flame is also capable of considerable adjustment in both character and power, features which, in conjunction with the simplicity, portability and low cost of the equipment, make the process extremely versatile and valuable for a wide variety of welding applications.

By referring to Fig. 6, it will be seen that the primary combustion of acetylene and oxygen (in the white 'cone' at the torch tip) produces hydrogen and carbon monoxide, both of which burn by absorbing oxygen from the atmosphere, producing carbon dioxide and water vapour (or steam) which form the bulk of the flame. The tip of the white cone is the point of highest temperature in the flame, and during welding the secondary combustion flame should cover the molten pool, protecting it from the oxidising and nitriding effects of the surrounding atmosphere. The flame may be adjusted to neutral (oxygen and acetylene equal), oxidising (excess of oxygen in the secondary zone) or carburising (excess of acetylene).

An incorrectly regulated flame may have a detrimental effect on the weld metal. Only one type of oxy-acetylene

Metal	Flame
Mild steel	Neutral
Stainless steels	,,
Cast iron	,,
Copper	,,
Aluminium	,,
Nickel alloys	,,
Monel	,,
Everdur	,,
Brass	Oxidising
Inconel	Slightly carburising
Aluminium alloys	,, ,,
Magnesium alloys	,, ,,

Table 2. Oxy-acetylene Flame Adjustments required for Various Metals.

welding application needs an oxidising flame – the welding of brass (page 99) and bronze non-fusion welding (pages 78, 86 and 98). For all other metals, an oxidising flame is harmful, and the tendency for the flame to become oxidising should be continually corrected; this can be done by maintaining a *slight* flicker at the end of the white cone (see page 90).

A definitely carburising flame has a useful application for the deposition of surfacing metals with surface fusion – the procedure is described on page 142.

The efficiency with which flame heat can be used depends on the melting point and thermal conductivity of the metal to be welded – the higher these factors are, the higher must be the flame temperature.* Generally, therefore, although the high temperature of the oxy-acetylene flame is advantageous for all metals, it is possible to use hydrogen or propane for some low melting point metals such as lead and zinc.

Today, oxy-acetylene welding is mostly applied to joints in sheet steel and non-ferrous metal products, and to a lesser extent for the repair of preheated iron and non-ferrous castings, the deposition of hard facing metals, and the non-fusion (bronze) welding of iron castings and steel parts. Other typical applications are the manufacture of chemical plant and tank linings in non-corrosive metals; copper piping systems; brass, aluminium alloy and other non-ferrous decorative metalwork; steel and non-ferrous pipework, steel tubular structures, etc.

Two procedures are in use: leftward, or forward, welding and rightward, or backward, welding, both of which are shown at A and B respectively in Fig. 7. It will be seen that in procedure A the flame is directed forward

* The same considerations do not apply to the use of these gases for oxygen cutting, since, in that application, the flame is not required to melt the metal, but only to preheat it and to make up for heat losses (see page 152).

over the unwelded portion of the joint, whereas in the procedure shown at B the flame covers the completed weld.

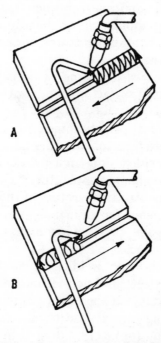

Fig. 7. Oxy-acetylene Welding.
A: Leftward or forward welding. B: Rightward or backward welding.

In forward welding, the flame preheats the unwelded edges but is also liable to create considerable distortion, and it is therefore always necessary to avoid excessive torch movement which might increase the heat spread. It is usually advantageous to incline the work surface slightly (about 10°) to minimise the risk of molten metal running forward between unmelted joint edges.

The backward method is most suitable for butt joints in steel over $\frac{3}{16}$ in [5 mm] thick, where it has the advantage of concentrating the flame heat between the joint edges (prepared to a 60° vee) and avoids the risk of molten metal running forward into unfused edges. Also, the operator is able to see the bottom edges of the vee, and to secure complete fusion and penetration without the necessity for a back run, this advantage being particularly useful for butt-welded pipe joints.

Except for edge joints such as those shown in Fig. 3, the addition of metal from a filler wire or rod is always necessary, and for most metals, except steel, a flux is also required. The flux is usually a powder, which may be mixed to a paste with alcohol or water and painted on joint edges and rod; flux-coated rods are also available. For the bronze welding process (see below) the necessary flux may be vaporised and applied by means of a gasflux dispenser, which enables the flux to be picked up by the oxygen flow through the hose and applied to the work via the flame.

Gas Non-fusion Welding

For repairing cast and malleable iron, joining sheet steel components, steel tubular structures and galvanised parts, and for rebuilding worn surfaces with a machinable and corrosion-resisting weld metal, the non-fusion bronze welding* process provides a quick, low-heat, strong joint. This process depends on the fact that a 60/40† brass welding rod (usually called bronze) forms a strong bond with steel or iron at approximately the melting temperature of the brass rod, i.e. about 900°C; thus the depositing surface is not melted, heating and distortion are minimised, and – provided that the surface is clean – the bond between it and the bronze provides a strong, reliable joint. This procedure has certainly made possible many iron casting repairs that would otherwise have been un-

* In American welding literature, often called 'braze welding'.
† That is, containing approximately 60% copper 40% zinc.

economical (see pages 126 and 135 for more details of its use in repair welding).

Non-fusion (bronze) welding can be used to join copper sheet and pipe (see page 98) and also to join dissimilar metals such as copper to steel and steel to cast iron.

*Gas Welding Equipment**

The simplest, most compact, portable and convenient basic oxy-acetylene welding (or cutting) unit consists of a cylinder each of compressed oxygen and acetylene, together with the necessary pressure regulators, hoses, torch or blowpipe. Oxygen cylinders are just steel bottles containing oxygen at about 2500 lbf/in² [175 bar]* when full. For large installations, the oxygen is usually supplied to take-off points by pipeline from a manifold of cylinders (page 19) or a liquid oxygen evaporator.

Acetylene compressed into cylinders is often known as 'dissolved acetylene' because the cylinders contain a porous filling material soaked in acetone, which will absorb or 'dissolve' twenty-five times its own volume of acetylene for every atmosphere of pressure applied; such cylinders are filled to approximately 300 lbf/in² (20·7 bar). Acetylene cylinders may be manifolded in the same way as oxygen cylinders, provided that suitable anti-flashback devices are incorporated in the system (see also page 165 *re* safety notes dealing with gas cylinders).

Whenever compressed gases are employed, a pressure 'regulator' is needed on the cylinder outlet to reduce the pressure of the gas leaving the cylinder to a lower (or 'working') pressure suitable for use in a welding, cutting or heating torch; such regulators also automatically maintain the working pressure more or less constant,

* Read the safety notes in Part 5 (page 162) before attempting to use gas or arc welding (or cutting) equipment.

† The metric pressure equivalent of 2500 lbf/in² is 172·5 bar, but in October 1971 the cylinder pressure was standardised at 175 bar.

even if the output demand fluctuates and the cylinder pressure falls. The output pressure is usually (but not necessarily) variable by means of a pressure-adjusting screw to suit the various nozzles used on the welding or cutting torch.

As shown in Fig. 8, the pressure regulators are fitted with two pressure gauges: one showing the cylinder pressure (or 'contents' in the case of oxygen cylinders) and the other the outlet, or 'working', pressure. In some types of regulator, the outlet pressures are marked on the barrel of the pressure-adjusting screw, so that an outlet pressure gauge is not necessary. Where the regulator is liable to be subjected to extremely rough usage, some operators prefer to dispense also with the contents gauge in order to minimise maintenance costs.

Very accurate and non-fluctuating regulation of gas output from a high pressure cylinder is obtained by using a two-stage regulator; such regulators are desirable for welding but are not necessary for cutting. Welding torches vary considerably in design, but they generally incorporate a range of different-sized nozzles, or tips, to enable the gas output, or power, of the torch to be varied to suit metals of differing melting points or thicknesses. Most cutting torches sold today are of the 'nozzle mix' type, i.e. the oxygen and fuel gas are mixed in the nozzle and the same torch can be used with either propane or acetylene as the fuel gas. It is, of course, essential to fit the appropriate type of nozzle for the fuel gas employed, and the correct size for the metal to be cut (pages 156 and 157).

Also available are nozzles for cutting steel up to $\frac{1}{8}$ in thick cleanly and with very little distortion; gouging nozzles for removing old welds, excess metal, or surface defects. For cutting torches using propane, heating nozzles can be fitted for bending or straightening; 'pepper pot' type heating nozzles are also available for oxy-acetylene welding torches.

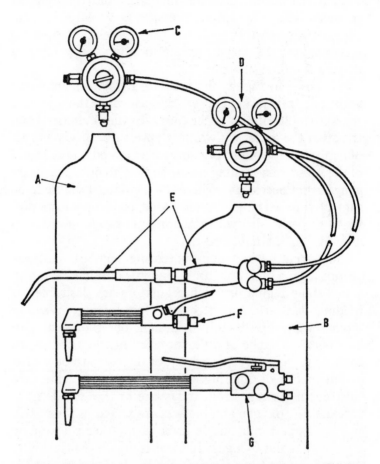

Fig. 8. Oxy-acetylene Welding/Cutting Equipment.

A: Oxygen cylinder. B: Acetylene cylinder (gas cylinders shown diagrammatically, cylinder valves omitted). C: Oxygen pressure regulator. D: Acetylene pressure regulator. E: Welding torch shank and welding tip. F: Cutting attachment which can be fitted to the above shank in place of the welding tip. G: Cutting torch (alternative to E and F).

See note re pressure regulators on previous page.

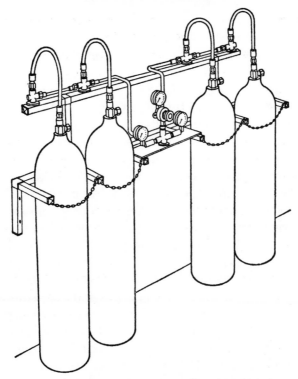

Fig. 9. A Typical Gas Cylinder Manifold.

A manifold such as this saves shop space, eliminates cylinder handling in the shop and avoids the hazard of having individual cylinders for each usage point. For maximum convenience the manifold should be located as near as possible to the cylinder off-loading and empty pick-up point. Any number of cylinders may be manifolded – the number of cylinders being decided by the rate of gas usage and the frequency of cylinder delivery. As shown above, the usual arrangement is to have the cylinders in two banks, one being in use while the other is in reserve or being changed for full ones; each bank has its own control valve and pressure gauge; for combustible gases flashback arrestors must be fitted. The cylinders are coupled to the manifold main by P.T.F.E.-lined flexible stainless steel braided hoses, suitable for either side or top entry cylinders. (*Pressure Control Ltd.*)

Fusion Arc Welding – Electrodes

In Fusion Arc Welding an arc is struck between a metal
wire, or 'electrode', and a metal workpiece, (electrode
and workpiece are connected by cables to the welding
plant, see Fig. 10, and thus become parts of the electrical
circuit). The arc heat melts the electrode tip and the
metal surface, the electrode melts and metal is deposited
– to build up a surface or weld joint edges together.

Obviously, the type of electrode employed is an important factor in arc welding. Originally, bare metal wires
were used as electrodes, but these produced an unsteady,
spattering arc, and the resultant deposits were usually
weak and brittle due to atmospheric contamination of
the molten metal.

The normal metal electrode is now provided with a
clay-like coating which produces gas and slag, stabilising
the arc and protecting the molten metal from atmospheric
contamination (see Fig. 5, page 9); the coating also minimises spatter and assists in the globular deposition of the
metal, allowing welds to be made on the vertical plane,
and even overhead, without undue difficulty. For easy
deposition, an electrode should be smooth-running, producing an easily removed or self-removing slag.

It should be appreciated that although all weld deposits consist of cast metal, the welded joint is usually
expected to have physical properties similar to those
of the workpiece. Therefore, the composition of the
deposit may be different from that of the workpiece,
since alloying elements are added from the electrode core
wire or coating to provide the weld characteristics required and to compensate for elements lost or modified
during welding.

In order to classify the various types of electrodes produced by different manufacturers, British Standard
Classifications have been prepared (see page 109).

Special low hydrogen coatings have been evolved

which minimise the production of hydrogen and water vapour, and avoid the tendency for welds in some steels to crack under cooling restraint. 'Deep penetration' steel electrodes are also available which produce two or three times the arc energy of normal electrodes and enable thick, close-butted, square-edge joints or tight fillets to be welded with exceptional penetration.

In normal manual arc welding, the welder ensures uniform fusion by maintaining a constant arc length between the electrode tip and the work surface; the introduction of 'touch' electrodes allows the core wire to melt back inside the coating, which rests on and is drawn along the work surface, reducing operator fatigue and facilitating high deposition rates with uniform fusion. 'Iron powder' electrodes, embodying up to 30% of the deposit metal in the coating, now provide partially conductive coatings, producing a secondary arc and facilitating sidewall fusion (or 'wetting') in fillet welding; they also increase the deposition rate and welding speed, reducing distortion and cost of welding (see also page 135).

Bronze electrodes are also available for welding together dissimilar metals, repairing iron, or bronze castings and rebuilding worn parts in steel, cast iron or bronze.

Most ferrous electrodes are suitable for a.c. (alternating current or d.c. (direct current). Bronze electrodes are also available for a.c. operation; otherwise, non-ferrous metals need d.c. When d.c. is used for nickel alloys the electrode should be positive, but for aluminium and bronze welding negative polarity minimises the burn-off rate.

Manual Arc Welding Equipment

A.c. equipment is probably suitable for 90% of all manual arc welding, d.c. only being essential when welding non-ferrous metals. A.c. equipment usually consists of a transformer operating off the single-phase mains electricity (Fig. 10), though three-phase transformers are also available; the output amperage of the unit can

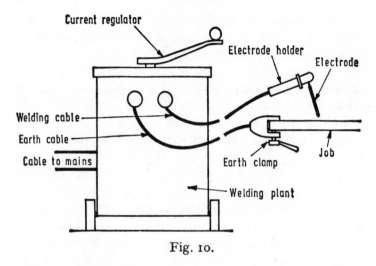

Fig. 10.

be varied either by a handle that operates a moving core or connects with tappings from the transformer, or the transformer casing may have a number of sockets of different amperage values into which the electrode holder lead may be plugged. These units may be either oil- or air-cooled; except for very small sets, oil cooling is preferable, especially for dusty or damp working conditions. Practically no maintenance is required, except that oil-cooled types need an oil change every twelve months or so – depending on how frequently the set is used. Although generally each transformer supplies one operator, two-operator units are available. The plant, and cables, should have sufficient amperage capacity for the largest electrode likely to be used (see Table 9, page 75).

D.c. equipment may consist of a motor-generator or a transformer unit incorporating a rectifier to give a d.c. output (a.c. welding transformers may also be converted to d.c. output by the addition of an a.c./d.c. convertor); combination transformers are also available, providing either a.c. or d.c. at the turn of a switch.

Area of core wire (copper)	Type of cable			Type of cable		
	VR/TRS (rubber) colour—black			EPR/CSP (synthetic rubber) colour—orange		
	Duty cycle†			Duty cycle†		
mm²	100%	50%	30%	100%	50%	30%
16	105	150	190	135	195	245
25	135	200	245	180	260	330
35	170	250	310	225	330	410
50	220	300	400	285	420	520
70	270	400	495	355	525	620

Table 3. Current-carrying Capacity of Copper* Welding Cables (ampères).

* Aluminium core wire cables also available.
† Duty cycle (see explanatory notes on page 25).
(Figures based on B.I.C.C. tables)

D.c. generators or a.c. transformers for shop use may operate off the usual electricity supply, but for portability or site work there are petrol, diesel or butane gas engine-driven generators. Ordinary electric generators are not suitable for arc welding; a properly designed arc welding generator must be used, and the engine must be matched to the generator as regards power required and correct speed.

Multi-operator a.c. equipment is available for use in shipyards and large workshops where several operators can be supplied from one transformer. Such equipment saves floor space, costs less than several individual trans-former units and – with a three-phase transformer – draws a balanced load from the supply.

Each operator is provided with a current regulator and, when circumstances permit, a common welding return current system is arranged, or separate return connections may be made from workpieces to transformer.

A large variety of electrode holders is available; generally speaking, the fully insulated types are the safest and well worth their higher cost. Both welding and earth cables must be adequate in cross-section to carry the current to be used; small cables create voltage drop – to the detriment of the work – if long lengths are involved.

Connections from the welding plant to the electrode holder and the earth clamp should be made efficiently to avoid current losses and overheating due to loose, dirty or corroded contacts at any point. For the same reason, a good earth clamp is desirable, and this should be firmly secured to a clean surface on the work.

A handshield or helmet is required – a helmet leaves both hands free and is not so liable to damage as a handshield. The coloured lens (see Specifications page 109, also table on page 173) should always be protected on the outside by a clear cover 'glass' which, to maintain good vision, should be renewed when it becomes spotted or discoloured. *Never* weld with a cracked or perforated coloured lens. Plastic lenses resist spatter and breakage better than glass but scratch more easily.

Welding slag can be removed with chipping hammer and wire brush or – more effectively and quickly – by a pneumatic needle descaling gun. Gauntlet gloves should be worn to protect the welder's hands, arms and sleeve ends from spatter; plastic surfaced leather gloves resist spatter better than plain leather and last longer.

Welding Cables

Two types of cable insulation are available: ordinary rubber and synthetic rubber. The synthetic insulation will withstand high core wire temperatures without deterioration, and this feature is used to rate the current capacity higher for the same size core wire. Therefore, although the cost of synthetic cable is slightly higher, this can often be offset by using a smaller size cable.

Duty cycle (Table 3) refers to the continuity of use to which the cable will be put, e.g. 100% means continuous use, 50% means 2½ minutes' use out of every 5 minutes, and 30% approximately 1½ minutes' use out of 5 minutes. For most everyday manual arc welding, the 50% rating will be ample for the average length of cable.

Other Manual Arc Welding Processes

The carbon arc and atomic hydrogen welding processes were fully described in the original editions of this book, but as they have been generally superseded by the more efficient inert gas-shielded arc processes, only a brief description of them is now necessary.

Carbon arc welding, using d.c. and a single carbon electrode, was applied in a generally similar way to oxy-

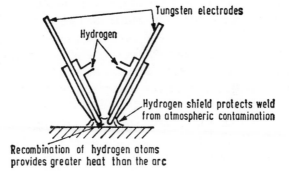

Fig. 11. Atomic Hydrogen Process

acetylene welding but, owing to its higher flame temperature, it was mainly applied to welding copper. Joints in thin metal could be prepared so that they did not require additional filler metal, as shown on page 7, otherwise a separate filler rod would be used.

The atomic hydrogen process used a special torch holding two tungsten electrodes with a nozzle arrangement feeding pure hydrogen to the arc zone (Fig. 11). The breakdown and recomposition of the gas increased the 'flame' temperature to about 4100°C, and provided an inert gas envelope covering the molten weld metal. High quality welds were produced in copper, steel and nickel alloys and, at one time, it was the only fusion process permitted for chain welding. Filler metal (if required) would be added from a separate welding wire or rod.

*Inert Gas-shielded Arc**

These are fusion welding procedures the basic feature of which is the envelopment of the arc and the weld pool by an inert gas, delivered to the weld point through the welding torch or gun; the molten metal is thus completely shielded from atmospheric contamination. Much higher welding speeds are obtainable than with normal gas or arc welding; consequently, there is less heat input to the workpiece and less distortion, and production costs are correspondingly reduced. Since no electrode coating or separate flux is required, even for non-ferrous metals, there is no risk of slag or flux trapping and no slag or residual flux to be removed after welding. Very high quality welds are therefore obtainable with a high degree of uniformity.

The shielding gas may be argon, helium, nitrogen or carbon dioxide, or mixtures of these gases, which are usually more effective and economical than the pure gas. For example, argon/CO_2 is used for steel, argon/oxygen for stainless steel and nitrogen/argon for copper.

Either a continuous consumable wire electrode or a tungsten electrode with separate feed wire may be used; these methods are usually referred to as MIG (i.e. metal inert gas) and TIG (tungsten inert gas) respectively.

* Complete details of the equipment, filler wires and welding techniques are beyond the scope of this book, and the reader is recommended to read the appropriate specialised literature available.

MIG welding wire is provided in coils (approx. 15 Kg per coil) from which it is fed to the torch at an automatically controlled rate. Deposit metal for TIG welding is provided by using lengths of wire as in oxy-acetylene welding. Indeed, O/A wires can be used, but special TIG wires are preferable.

A.c. is generally used with tungsten electrodes and d.c. with the consumable metal wire electrode; a.c. arc stability is usually improved by superimposing a high frequency (h.f.), high voltage current on the welding current; this also avoids the contamination of the electrode or workpiece by contact, since the arc may then be initiated without touching the electrode on the work.

Although the TIG process has many economical applications, the MIG process finds increasing application due to its higher speed – and therefore reduced distortion – and adaptability to fillet and positional welding.

The best results with high speeds and the minimum of distortion are obtained when the processes are mechanised, but manual application is also extensively employed for fabrication work. For metal $\frac{1}{8}$ in [3 mm] thick or more, normal MIG equipment usually employs a 'self-adjusting' arc, which compensates for irregularities in the distance between electrode tip and work surface, the burn-off rate being dependent on the arc length. This principle makes it possible to machine weld irregular-shaped assemblies, with the torch guided over the contour of the joint by means of a template.

Feed wires $\frac{1}{16}$ in [1·6 mm] diameter and upwards (for welding metals over about $\frac{3}{16}$ in [5 mm] thick) are usually fed to the torch from a remote reel, but the fine wire required for thin gauge metal is more conveniently fed from a wire spool incorporated in the gun itself.*

---

* The use of fine wire MIG welding of thin sheet has led to the development of specialised techniques and equipment. Whereas the arc manipulation and metal transfer for thicker plate is similar

The torch may be water- or air-cooled, air cooling being suitable for currents up to 200 ampères (abbreviation A); miniature torches for use with very low current on delicate work are also available. To ensure an accurate flow the argon is supplied through a two-stage regulator fitted with a flowmeter, the consumption varying from 7–20 ft³/h (3·3–9·4 litre/min); welding current will range from 40 to 750 A, depending on the thickness and type of metal being welded.

Unless complete weather protection is provided, argon is not generally suitable for outdoor work, since even a slight wind will easily disperse the gas shield; carbon dioxide is better than argon in this respect.

CO_2 Welding

The high weld quality and reduced production costs obtained by using the gas-shielded arc (MIG) are advantageous even for steel, where the fluxing requirements are not as critical as they are for light alloys and corrosion-resistant metals; however, the high cost of argon makes this gas generally uneconomical for steel. The much cheaper CO_2 (carbon dioxide) is therefore used, with deoxidised wire.

High currents are used with comparatively small wire,

---

to that used for normal manual arc welding, for thin sheet – due to the exceptionally low currents and voltages, and the short arc employed – a short-circuiting arc technique is used, the metal being deposited by dip transfer or by contact between the electrode end and the molten pool, power being supplied by slope-controlled rectifiers.

The arc heat is highly localised, giving excellent control of penetration for fillet and positional welding with the minimum heating of metal ahead or at the sides of the weld point. Exceptionally high speeds – up to 10 ft/min [3 m/min] – with almost no distortion are therefore possible, and the lower power arc and ease of manipulation enable a wide variation in fit-up gap to be tolerated – an unusual advantage in arc welding processes.

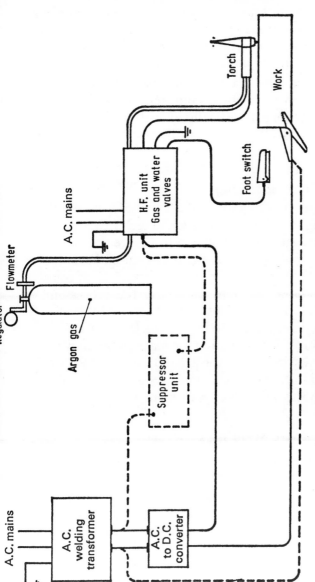

Fig. 12. Inert Gas Arc Welding.

General arrangement of typical argon arc equipment using an air-cooled tungsten electrode torch. Connections for both A.C. and D.C. are shown. The suppressor unit is only necessary for welding aluminium and magnesium base alloys, and for aluminium bronze where the refractory oxide film requires the use of a balanced current waveform. (*Messrs. Max Arc Ltd.*)

thus providing a high degree of penetration, which is particularly useful for fillet welds and close butt joints.

Manual d.c./CO_2 welding equipment is capable of depositing up to 18 lb (8·2 kg) of metal per hour, and excellent results are obtained from mechanised welding. For example, with a twin-head machine $\frac{5}{8}$ in [16 mm] plate may be welded vertically at 21 ft/h (6·4 m/h) in a single pass, and fillet welds can be made at the rate of 1–3 ft/min (0·3–0·9 m/min).

Inert Gas Arc Spot Welding

The inert gas tungsten arc process can also be used for spot welding; a special torch is employed with a suitable nozzle which enables the sheets to be pressed together by manual pressure. A.c. or d.c. may be used in conjunction with a timer and contactor unit. Fusion is, of course, from one side of the joint only, and the process may be used for mild and stainless steel sheets up to $\frac{1}{16}$ in [1·6 mm] or for joining sheet to heavier sections. It is not at present suitable for aluminium or magnesium alloys.

On the following pages, the principal mechanised welding processes are described briefly. See also page 49 for reference to the latest development in TIG welding.

Mechanised Arc Welding Processes

With improvements in electronic controls, mechanised automatic or semi-automatic arc welding processes are now used for welding operations previously applied manually, such as circumferential and longitudinal welds of tanks and pressure vessels, fillet welds of bulkhead and deck stiffeners, the fabrication of built-up structural sections*, and the repair of worn parts. Many arc and gas

* For this and other similar applications, twin-head machines are available, enabling two opposing fillets to be made simultaneously, thus minimising distortion.

welding applications on sheet metals, particularly car body repairs, corrosion-resisting and non-ferrous metals, are being replaced by inert gas arc welding, and manual welding on steel plate is being superseded by submerged arc or CO_2 arc welding.

The use of mechanised welding is, of course, dependent on existing equipment, operator skills and other facilities that may already be available, and the economics of the cost of new equipment must be considered in relation to the cost, quantity and importance of the work being done; also to the improved quality, uniformity, high speed and reduced distortion of the welds obtained.

Submerged Arc Welding
This is an automatic process, developed primarily for the production of high-quality welds in thicker steel plate than is normally suited to manual arc welding. Steel plate up to 3 in [75 mm] thick may be welded in one pass, and the process has also been applied to nickel alloys and

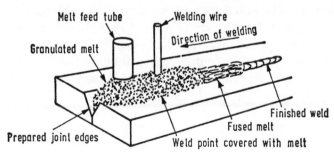

Fig. 13. Submerged Arc Welding.

aluminium bronzes. It is largely used for butt and fillet welds in the construction of boilers and other pressure vessels, tanks, piping, ships decking and prefabricated sections; for the assembly of forgings; and for the repetition rebuilding of worn caterpillar track pins, rollers and rings.

The arc is formed between the end of a continuous bare wire electrode and the plate edges or depositing surface under a layer of protective powder, known as the flux or 'melt', which can also be used to add alloying elements to the weld metal. The flux powder is fed continuously onto the joint ahead of the welding wire, and while the weld is being made the arc is submerged under the powder and is invisible. Fusion of the powder surrounding the end of the wire and arc produces a slag which protects the molten weld metal from atmospheric contamination and retards its cooling rate; when the weld has cooled, the slag peels off without the need for chipping, and any un-fused powder can be recovered for re-use. Very high welding speeds are obtained with very good quality weld metal, which, although coarse in grain structure, satisfies in all respects the usual requirements for pressure vessel construction.

Although the process is particularly suited to thick plate welding, with small wires and low amperages it can be used with equal success for thin plate and small fillet welding – for example, 12 s.w.g. [2·5 mm] plate can be welded at speeds of up to 8 ft (2·4 m) per minute.

D.c. is normally employed, although there may be applications where a.c. is preferable; very high welding currents are used – up to as much as 4000 A – depending on the wire size and the thickness to be welded, the arc and the wire feed speed being automatically regulated by a voltage control unit.

The process may be applied manually, but usually the welding head is power driven, the welding rate being automatically controlled according to the current used.

Joints must be arranged for downhand welding, and internal or external longitudinal joints of cylindrical weldments are usually made by moving the welding head along a boom track over the joint; pipe down to 14 in [355 mm] inside diameter can be welded in this way. For circumferential welds or for building up cylindrical parts, the workpiece must be rotated under a stationary welding head; for flat plate joints, such as ships decking, the welding head is often mounted on a mechanically propelled carriage, which runs on the plate surface and can be steered to follow any irregularities in the joint. Twin-head machines are also available for making two

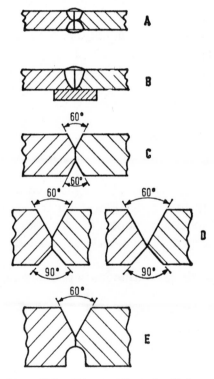

Fig. 14. Plate Edge Preparations for Submerged Arc Welding.

A & C: Machine weld both sides: A up to $\frac{1}{2}$ in [12 mm] thick; C up to 2 in [50 mm] thick. B: Machine weld one side up to $\frac{1}{2}$ in [12 mm] thick. D: Main machine weld with manual backing weld up to $1\frac{1}{4}$ in [32 mm] thick. E: Over $1\frac{1}{4}$ in [32 mm] thick.

longitudinal or circumferential butt or fillet welds simultaneously.

Up to ¾ in [20 mm] thick square joint edges may be used; above that thickness, the edges must be double bevelled and, although the main weld may be made in one pass, a backing weld is always necessary (see Fig. 14).

Submerged arc equipment is frequently arranged so that it can be readily converted to open arc welding using fluxed wire, or with special heads for CO_2 welding, and some machines are also adaptable for use with flame-cutting heads.

Electro-slag Welding

This is an automatic, machine-operated procedure for the butt joining of very thick steel plates to produce heavy steel fabrications, such as thick-walled pressure vessels, heavy machinery frames, etc. In principle, the process involves the continuous casting of weld metal between square plate edges, the weld being carried out in a single pass, vertically upwards. Plates up to 15 in [380 mm] thick can be welded without difficulty and, since no edge bevelling is needed, there is very little cost in the preparation of plate edges.

One, two or three continuous wire or strip electrodes – using up to 1000 A per electrode – can be used, according to the thickness being welded. An important aspect of the process is the simplicity of preparation and setting up; the width of the gap between the edges is not critical, and is usually between ½ in [10 mm] and 1½ in [40 mm] depending on the plate thickness. Maintenance of the gap, and alignment of the plate edges throughout the weld, is secured by welded-on clamps.

The process may be initiated by striking an arc between the electrodes and a starting block under a layer of powdered flux; this is done between a pair of run-on plates to allow the arc to be stabilised and adjustments to be made outside the actual joint. Run-off plates are also provided at the other end of the joint, both run-on and run-off plates being removed after the joint is completed. Powder is added, and the submerged arc runs until sufficient depth of slag has formed and the plate edges begin to melt; the process then automatically changes over to full electro-slag welding, the heat to maintain the weld pool and melt the joint edges and the electrode wires being derived from the energy released by the passage of current through the molten slag. The molten weld metal is supported by water-cooled copper shoes, which bridge the back and front of the gap between

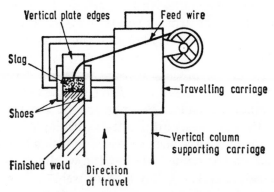

Fig. 15. Electro-slag Welding.

the edges. These shoes, together with the electrode feed carriage, are automatically moved upwards as the weld metal is melted into the joint, and the lower portion of the deposited metal solidifies. On thick welds, the electrodes are also given a continuous slow oscillation across the gap in order to distribute the heat throughout the weld metal pool and maintain uniform melting of the joint edges. A little extra flux may be needed as the weld proceeds; this can be provided by using a composite feed wire incorporating make-up flux.

Very little metal from the joint edges is melted and the

weld is substantially rectangular in section, i.e. the width of the front and back of the weld is the same. Distortion is therefore minimised and contraction, which tends to reduce the gap as the weld proceeds, can be counteracted by setting the gap on a taper.

The process is highly efficient, since more metal may be deposited per 100 A of current than with any other process. Metal deposition rate may be as high as 40–90 lb (18·1–40·8 kg) per hour, with welding speeds of up to 3 m per hour, and present indications are that even higher rates and speeds may be achieved.

Since there is no agitation of the molten pool, the weld metal is slag free and, with the surface of the weld pool protected from the atmosphere by the slag, there should be no porosity; however, hot cracking may occur with faulty technique.

The use of the process appears to be limited by the poor impact properties of the welds obtained – compared with normal arc welds. Normalising is therefore indicated; this may present difficulties with large structures but good results have been obtained by using a gas torch fitted into the machine to follow the welding head.

Although intended mainly for butt welds, tee welds can also be made (without any plate preparation) and, by suitable arrangement and shaping of the weld metal-retaining shoes, various shapes of build-up can be cast onto the surface of a plate or existing section.

The vertical welding principle in this process has also been developed as a direct arc welding process in connection with a CO_2 shrouded arc, producing very high welding speeds in joining thick plates in a single pass.

Welds Involving Mechanical Pressure

Welds may be made by pressing two pieces of metal together while current (a.c.) is passed across the joint;

the resistance to the passage of the current from one piece to the other creates heat at the contacting surfaces, raising them to melting temperature; mechanical pressure is applied to force the molten surfaces together, completing the weld. This is resistance welding.

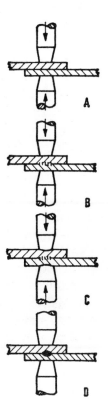

Fig. 16. Spot Welding Sequence.

A: Pressure applied to electrodes; current 'off'. B: Current 'on' and joint surfaces heated. C: Joint surfaces melt, current 'off'. D: Weld solidifies, current 'off' and electrode pressure released.

This principle is applicable to the lap jointing of sheet metals and to the direct end-to-end butt jointing of bars, tubes and similar shapes. It is essentially a local heating operation; heavy currents are employed, the heat developed depending on the current intensity and 'on' time, and the joint resistance.

Spot Welding

This is the simplest method of applying the process to lap joints for the manufacture of all kinds of sheet metal products where a gas- or liquid-tight joint is not required.

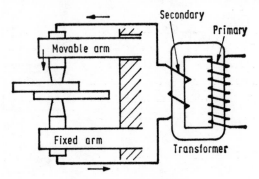

Fig. 17. Spot Welding.

The joint surfaces are pressed together between the tips of two opposing copper alloy rod-type electrodes. Current is switched 'on' until the joint surfaces melt, forming a weld metal 'nugget'; current is then switched 'off', and mechanical pressure is maintained until the weld solidifies and is strong enough to hold the joint. The current 'on' and 'off' and 'hold' times, and the electrode pressure, must be varied according to the thickness and type of metal being welded.

Stitch Welding

Many spot welders are also adapted to stitch welding, which is an automatic form of spot welding in that, once the operation has been initiated, a control mechanism takes over and automatically repeats the weld cycle up to as many as 300 spots per minute for any desired period. This procedure may either be applied to individually spaced spots or the spots may be overlapped to produce a continuous weld.

Seam Welding

This is a similar process, except that the lap joint is pressed together by a pair of wheels, or a wheel and a mandrel. While the wheels rotate and the seam moves between them, a series of high current pulsations are applied, producing a continuous liquid- and pressure-tight joint. Either straight or circumferential seams of containers or piping may be welded in this way, and

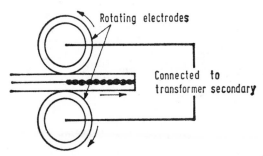

Fig. 18. Seam Welding.

wheels may be cut away to enable joints to be taken right into corners.

Projection Welding

Projection welding is a development of spot welding; one of the joint surfaces is plain, the other is provided with one or more raised projections, or pimples, at the points where the welds are required. The electrodes may be round or rectangular copper alloy pads, which may also be designed to suit the shape of the parts being welded. Application of pressure to the electrodes and the passage of current from one electrode to the other causes the projections to melt and collapse, forming a weld.

The process is extensively used for the assembly of pressed or stamped parts, or for attaching pads, bosses, brackets, handles or studs to sheet metal articles; another application is cross-wire welding for the manufacture of wire products.

Spot, stitch, seam and projection welding processes are applicable to mild steel, stainless steel, aluminium, copper and nickel alloys, and are extensively used in the automobile, domestic appliance, chemical, aircraft, radio, refrigerator and jet engine industries. In the case of steel, spot welding may be used for joints up to $\frac{3}{8}$ in $+ \frac{3}{8}$ in

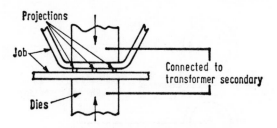

Fig. 19. Projection Welding.

[10 mm + 10 mm] thick; in aluminium, the maximum thickness would be about $\frac{3}{16}$ in $+ \frac{3}{16}$ in [5 mm + 5 mm], although the average thickness is probably 10 gauge [3·25 mm] or less. The joining parts may be equal or unequal in thickness.

Resistance Butt Welding
In this process, the two parts to be joined are held end-to-end in copper clamps, one fixed and one movable. Current is passed through the workpieces until the joint surfaces reach forging temperature; current is then switched off and more pressure is applied to force the two surfaces together, making an upset weld. This process is applied to the butt joining of mild steel wires and small bars in chain making, and the manufacture of wire products; it is also used for joining copper, bronze and brass wires, bars and sections.

Flash Butt Welding

In this process, the joint surfaces are heated by arcing, not by electrical resistance only. The parts to be joined – held in suitably shaped clamps or dies – are brought together and the current is switched on for a predetermined time; while the current is still flowing, the joint surfaces are separated, creating an arc between the butting surfaces. Arcing is allowed to continue until the surfaces melt uni-

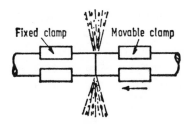

Fixed clamp   Movable clamp

Fig. 20. Flash Welding.

formly; current is then cut off and the surfaces are forced together, squeezing out slag and molten metal and producing a very high quality weld with a narrow heat-affected zone. Flash welds are being increasingly used for widely different jointing requirements, such as steel and stainless steel sheet metal shapes, rolled sections, forgings, rails,* bars and pipes. The process is also applicable

* British Rail (to whom the author is indebted for the following information) use 60 ft (18·3 m) flat bottomed rails, flash welded into lengths of 2 miles (3·22 km) or more. Briefly, the procedure consists of grinding the rail ends clean, with particular attention to the removal of rust; the rails are then clamped in the flash welding machine, leaving about ⅛ in [3 mm] between ends. The current is switched on, and the ends brought together and then separated. Arcing or flashing commences and continues until fusion occurs, at which point 40 tons (40·6 tonnes) end-to-end pressure is applied. Finally, the upset metal is removed and the joint electrically heated to 1650°F [900° C] to anneal the weld; the joint is ground to profile and any distortion corrected. Test welds are made four times daily and tup tested.

to the joining of non-ferrous metals, bars and sections – for example, it is extensively used for the manufacture of aluminium windows and dairy plant, and for joining heavy section nickel alloy rings. Machines capable of welding steel sections up to 40 in² (258 cm²) in area have been made.

Resistance Welding Equipment

Spot, stitch, seam and projection welding machines are virtually precision machine tools in that modern industrial requirements have become increasingly exacting; greater thickness are being welded, and mass production requirements involve heavy duty operating conditions.

Although operation may be electro-mechanical, the trend is to use air pressure for the electrode movement, thereby providing accurate adjustment of electrode force, reducing operator fatigue and, in conjunction with thyratron or ignitron current control, permitting operating speeds unobtainable with mechanical operation. Also, apart from the foot switch or other initiation control, the weld cycle is better controlled by an electronic timer, which provides infinite adjustment and precise control of squeeze, weld, hold and off times, according to the nature of the job and the metal being welded.

Electrically, spot welding machines may be classified in three types:

1. Single-phase a.c. machines: the majority of general purpose machines are of this type. They are intended to operate on single phase or on any two phases of a three-phase supply. Current is supplied from a built-in transformer, provided with secondary tappings to enable the current to be adjusted according to the metal and thickness to be welded. Very high welding current requirements may necessitate two or three transformers.

2. Three-phase a.c. machines: this type of machine is unusual at present as it is expensive and of comparatively recent development. Its outstanding advantages are that it draws a balanced load from the mains supply; the welding current is stepless and can be controlled readily and accurately; and it is cheap to run.
3. D.c. machines: these machines are intended for specialised work and are outside the scope of this book.

In all but the smallest spot welders, electrodes are generally water-cooled, and a large variety of different-shaped tips is available to suit surface contours and to enable the electrode to reach positions having limited accessibility. Correct and accurate shaping of the contact tip of the electrode is an important factor in securing good welds, especially with non-ferrous metals. Machines for welding light alloys are usually specially designed in order to apply the high currents required and provide the sensitive controls that are necessary for soft, low melting point metals.

The automobile industry, in which resistance welding is used extensively, has been responsible for the introduction of several special types of machine to suit its unusual requirements, and to avoid preliminary jigging and tacking. Portable spot welders are employed to enable the process to be used on assemblies too large or too heavy to be taken to a stationary machine. Many of these are specially designed to suit the work on which they are used and may be provided with various interchangeable lengths of arm to give a variety of throat clearances.

On the other hand, there are multi-head spot welders that enable all the spots needed for the welding of a large assembly to be made at one stroke. For example, one of the developments in the original production of Mini cars was a 40 ft (12·2 m) long, electronically controlled, five-stage transfer machine for the assembly and welding of complete sub-frame units, comprising twelve pressed parts and two sub-assemblies, on a production basis of 3000 units per 40-hour week.

Twin-stitch and seam welders are frequently employed for making duplicate welds on large components.

Stud Welding

This is a semi-automatic arc welding process for attaching studs or pins to steel plate, sections, pipe or weldments quickly and without preparation of the base to which the stud is welded.

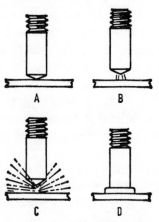

Fig. 21. Stud Welding.

A: Stud (held in gun) in contact with plate. B: Stud raised, creating pilot arc. C: Full welding current 'on', producing power arc which melts end of stud and plate surface. D: Stud released, current 'off' and weld completed.

(*Crompton Parkinson Ltd.*)

The resultant weld is stronger than the stud itself and, since the weld does not perforate the plate, there is no possibility of leakage at the point of attachment. Heavy components do not have to be moved to drilling and tapping machines; studs can be applied at any conven-

Metal	Fusion processes					Non-fusion oxy-acet. (bronze)	Resistance processes	
	Metal arc	Oxy-acet.	Inert gas arc	Sub-merged arc	Electro-slag		Spot seam	Flash
Mild steel	E	E*	E*†	E	E	E	E	E
High tensile steel	E‡	E*‡	—	E	E	E	E	E
Heat and corrosion-resistant stainless steels	G	F	E	—	E	E	E	G
Nickel and n. alloys	G§	G§	E	G	—	—	E	G
Copper	G§	G§	E	—	—	E	P	—
Brass	F	G	—	—	—	—	F	—
Aluminium and al. alloys	G	G	E	—	—	—	G	G
Cast iron	F	E‡	—	—	—	E‡	—	—

Table 4. The Weldability of Metals by Various Processes.

E = Excellent   F = Fair   G = Good   P = Poor

* Up to about ¼ in [6 mm].
† With CO_2 shield.
‡ Preheating and slow cooling may be necessary.
§ Not recommended if inert gas arc processes available.

ient stage of assembly and access is needed to only one side of the job. Although mostly used for steel studs, brass and copper studs can be welded to steel or copper sheet, and excellent results have also been obtained with aluminium bronze and silicon bronze studs.

The equipment consists of a 'gun' fitted with a chuck to receive the stud and a cable connected to a suitable d.c. power source, which incorporates the essential timing control equipment.

The process is speedy and simple; apart from inserting a stud in the chuck of the gun, locating it and pressing the operating button, the entire process is automatic, the actual welding cycle taking less than a second to complete; again, in a matter of seconds, a new stud can be inserted in the gun ready to repeat the operation.

Several welding methods are in use: in one, a stud is held in contact with the plate and a comparatively low current circulated by way of stud and plate. The stud then lifts and a pilot arc is struck, forming an ionised path on which the full welding arc is imposed; after an automatically controlled arcing period, the stud is again pressed onto the plate and the current is cut off. In another method, the lifting and return of the stud is also controlled automatically, but a pilot arc is not struck, the full welding current being imposed as soon as the operating button is pressed.

Studs must be of weldable quality metal, e.g. not high sulphur, carbon or lead content; specially prepared studs and screws are not required because the weld is initiated and controlled by a cartridge placed round the stud and in contact with the base to which it is to be welded. One of the more recent developments is to use argon shielding for stud welding on light alloys.

With another system, studs up to $\frac{1}{4}$ in [6 mm] in diameter may be welded to metals as thin as 0·020 in [0·5 mm] without distortion or weld burn. No flux, ferrules or inert gases are necessary, the welds being produced by discharging low voltage, high amperage d.c. through a patented tip on the stud. The tip initiates the arc on contact with the metal, melting the face of the stud and a similar area of the workpiece. The technique is suitable for welding aluminium, mild steel, brass, copper, titanium, etc.

A recent application is the welding of shear connectors for composite construction work. These are large diameter studs with cold forged heads on the free end, which act as anchors between steel beams and concrete slabs cast in the beams. For this work, the very heavy currents required (up to about 4700 A) necessitate special high-output transformer rectifiers.

Other Welding Processes

Thermit Welding
Thermit welding is an old-established fusion process originally devised for the end-to-end joining of tramway and railway rails, and ships' propeller shafts.

Basically the process is dependent on the great heat evolved from the fusion of a mixture of powdered aluminium and iron oxide; the ends of the parts to be joined are inserted into a sand or graphite mould, and the mixture is poured into a cavity or crucible above the joint. Fusion of the mixture is initiated by means of a small quantity of ignition powder, composed mainly of barium peroxide. The heat of the reaction reduces the iron oxide, and the resulting molten 'steel' is run into the mould, where it preheats and finally fuses and mixes with the ends of the bar or rail, forming a continuous joint.

Obviously, some time is occupied in raising the temperature of the joint to fusion point, and one of the modern developments of the process has been to reduce the preheat time in order to speed up the jointing time. This has been done with such effectiveness that a 94 lb

(42·6 kg) rail joint can be completed in 12 minutes, an operation that, without preheat, previously took an hour. For field work, oxy-propane burners provide a very convenient and portable means of preheating.

In factories the process is used for such jobs as the repair of broken parts of heavy machinery and the fabrication of machinery parts too large to be forged or cast economically in one piece; shafts as large as 36 in [915 mm] diameter have been repaired. Preheating of such parts may take several days, using propane and low pressure air from a centrifugal blower.

Although primarily for joining ferrous parts, in the U.S.A. the joining of copper cables, using copper oxide instead of iron oxide, is claimed to be a satisfactory application.

Ultrasonic Welding
This is a development of resistance spot welding – a form of cold pressure welding using spot welding-type electrodes without the passage of current, one of the electrodes being subjected to ultrasonic vibrations at a frequency above the audible limit. The method is only suitable for lap joints with single spots or continuous seams. Commercial aluminium sheet up to about $\frac{1}{8}$ in [3 mm] thick has been successfully welded in this way, and the process is also applicable to copper and nickel alloys.

Cold Welding
This is also a lap jointing process, welds being made by mechanical pressure only, without heat or current. The mechanical pressure deforms the metal so that plastic flow takes place and the metals unite. Appreciable deformation in thickness is unavoidable, but this is usually not detrimental for the purposes to which the process would be applied.

Cold welding is particularly applicable to aluminium and the softer aluminium alloys, and has also been applied very successfully to the sealing of foil containers and sheaths, and the making up of small electrical components and other items where a normal welding heat application is not permissible. No flux is required, but clean, non-oxidised jointing surfaces are essential to promote intimate metal contact. The necessary metal flow can be produced by hand tools or presses for the softer metals, but hard alloys need mechanised presses.

Oxy-acetylene Pressure Welding
Oxy-acetylene flames may be used for end-to-end joining; the components are clamped and multi-flame burners heat the metal until it reaches fusion point. Mechanical pressure is then applied, producing an upset joint. Rails, bars and pipes may be joined and the process has been used for steel, copper and copper alloys and dissimilar metals.

Pulsed Arc Welding
In this TIG welding technique, the arc current alternates between two levels, heating and fusion occurring during the peak periods while cooling and solidification takes place during the base periods. The operator has complete control over the wave form and obviously the waves must overlap to ensure a continuous weld. The main advantages of the technique are that the rate of heat input is reduced: and heat build-up along the weld is eliminated so that distortion is reduced. The operator's control over metal transfer and penetration can ensure a weld with minimum underbead.

Thick to thin thickness can be welded and the improved control of the weld pool reduces weld bead concavity, especially when welding tubular sections. The quality of TIG welds on mild and stainless steels, cupronickel alloys, aluminium, copper, and Berylium-copper alloys is greatly improved, and it is possible to use stick electrodes if desired.

Part 2

Welding for Manufacture

Good welding often starts at the design stage, where the accessibility and strength of the joint, cost and the effectiveness of the welding process are often decided by the number, type and location of the joints. It is, therefore, reasonable to presume that the designer of a welded product should have some practical experience of welding and some knowledge of the various welding processes that are available – particularly those in his own plant – and will understand their various advantages and limitations, and the joint preparations required. He should also know something about metals, their weldability, limitations and reactions to welding. Briefly, here are some of the considerations involved.

Designing for Welding

When considering the application of welding to the construction of components or plant originally produced by other methods, it is usually desirable to modify the design to facilitate production and to take full advantage of the benefits to be gained by using welding.

Intelligent design will simplify inspection after welding and, by careful consideration of the location of the joint, reduce the necessity for correction of dimensional or shape errors arising from distortion. Overwelding and unnecessary welds will be minimised by utilising bent sheets and plates to eliminate corner welds, and by incorporating rolled sections to reduce fillet welding.

Accessibility will also have to be considered in order to allow the operator the necessary freedom to manipulate the electrode or torch, to see what he is doing, to jig or clamp the joint, and to enable after-welding inspection and operations such as chipping, grinding or peening (if required) to be carried out easily. For example, with spot welding it is necessary to ensure accessibility for the top and bottom electrodes (as shown in Fig. 22).

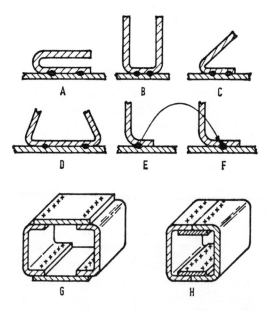

Fig. 22. Designing for Resistance Spot Welding.

A, B, C & D: Types of joints to avoid. E: Narrow flange causes spot to be located too near radius. F: Wider flange enables spot to be properly located. G & H: Types of design which may involve difficulties due to possible lack of accessibility for lower electrode.

In the case of weldments necessitating the use of corrosive fluxes (i.e. aluminium and magnesium alloys), care must be taken to avoid designs that involve corners, crevices, flanges or enclosures which may cause flux entrapment or be inaccessible for adequate washing after welding (see Fig. 45, page 100).

From the cost aspect, intermittent welds (fillets) may be preferred to continuous welds for some applications, e.g. tank bulkhead and deck stiffeners (Fig. 31). But, on the other hand, such welds should not be used where it may be desirable to seal a joint against the effects of rust or corrosion, and in any case it is often more satisfactory and economical to use a small continuous fillet than an intermittent large fillet.

It will be seen from the foregoing that correct design, taking into account the practical requirements of the welding process and the advantages offered by it, the characteristics of the metals involved and the end use of the weldment, is essential for the economical and efficient use of welding.

Edge preparation	Ratio of weight or volume of weld metal required
60° single vee 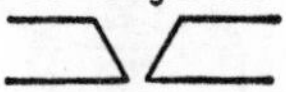	1
60° double vee 	·5
90° single vee 	1·65

Fig. 23. Influence of joint edge preparation on amount of weld metal required (see also page 72), assuming same thickness in each case.

Courses in welding technology and design are offered by the Welding Institute (see page 112). In addition to the various textbooks available, much useful information can be obtained from the literature published by the manufacturers and technical advisory bodies concerned with the development of uses for various metals (see page 171). The various welding specifications of the British Standards Institution are also essential references on all aspects of welding, since they embody the recommendations of both users and manufacturers of welding plant and materials, weldable metals and welded products (see page 109).

Preparing for Welding

Types of Joint

Butt (i.e. edge-to-edge) welds are preferable for fusion-welded joints in sheet or plate products such as pressure vessels, pipelines, decking, tanks and similar types of construction where continuity of section is important; fillet, lap and corner joints are generally applicable to the production of fabricated weldments, welded machinery components, the attachment of flanges and plate stiffeners, the assembly of rolled section and tubular building structures. Lap joints are an essential requirement for the seam and spot welding of sheet metals.

Welding time, heat input, distortion and cost of a weld are in the same ratio as the volume of metal required for the type of preparation used. Notice how the double vee halves the amount of weld metal required, while an increase in vee angle from 60° to 90° increases the weld metal required by at least 65% (see page 52).

Preparation of Welding Joints

All joint surfaces and edges to be welded need to be clean to avoid contamination of the weld metal and to obtain the maximum efficiency from the welding process employed. If the jointing surfaces are not clean, scale may cause adhesion, and gas-forming substances, e.g. paint or oil, may cause porosity or make it difficult to ensure efficient fusion between the deposit and the base metal. Surface dirt, scale, rust, grease or oil, protective coating or oxide skin should be removed by grinding, scratch brushing or, in special circumstances, by using degreasing agents, such as trichlorethlene or carbon tetrachloride.*

Sheet metals intended for spot or fusion welding do not usually require any further preparation, apart from ensuring that the joints, edges or laps are free from buckle and meet evenly throughout their length. For fusion welding, the edge joints shown in Fig. 3 are useful in that they stiffen the joint edges and enable the weld to be made without added filler metal, but they (also lap and tee fillet joints) should not be used for ordinary gas or arc welding of aluminium, owing to the risk of trapping flux, or for containers, where corrosive solids might be trapped.

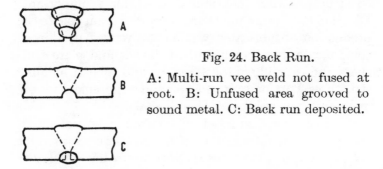

Fig. 24. Back Run.

A: Multi-run vee weld not fused at root. B: Unfused area grooved to sound metal. C: Back run deposited.

When the metal thickness exceeds $\frac{3}{16}$ in [5 mm] or thereabouts (depending on the process), edges intended to be butt jointed and fusion welded usually need to be bevelled or grooved in order to ensure that the welding heat and the weld metal reach and fuse the root of the joint, otherwise lack of fusion at that point will seriously weaken the weld.

For most welding processes, the welding speed, electrode or filler rod consumption, heat input and weld contraction are all proportional to the volume of weld metal required, i.e. the cross-sectional area and length of the

* Such liquids, if used, must be completely vaporised from the workpiece before welding, otherwise phosgene may be produced – with danger to the welder.

weld. Therefore, in order to secure the maximum welding economy and to minimise distortion, joints require the minimum of added weld metal consistent with adequate fusion and strength. Unnecessarily large vees or fillets waste weld metal,* increase cost and distortion, and may even reduce the strength of the joint, due to lack of fusion, excessive penetration or undercutting. The exact vee angle required varies according to the metal being welded and the process employed; one type of preparation does not suit all metals and processes, as will be seen by the preparation diagrams given for the different metals on the following pages.

One of the advantages of the mechanised welding processes – such as the submerged arc – is that greater thicknesses of plate can be welded without bevelling; the use of deep penetration manual welding electrodes also enables greater thicknesses of close-butted, square-edge steel plates to be welded than is possible with normal electrodes.

Bevelling and grooving may be done by machining, machine gas cutting, flame gouging, grinding or chipping; whatever method is employed, it is important to ensure that the preparation of each edge is the same, accurate and uniform throughout the joint.

Joint Fit-up

A good fit-up of the joint is always important, especially for manual arc welding. Any gap between butt joint edges should be uniform throughout the length of the joint, but for fillet welds a close joint is usually desirable, since a gap reduces the effective size of the fillet (see Fig. 25). Alignment of butt joint edges is very important for both the appearance and the strength of the finished weld, and should, if possible, be ensured by using suitable clamps or tacking, or by holding the joint edges in a jig

* See page 52.

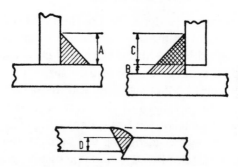

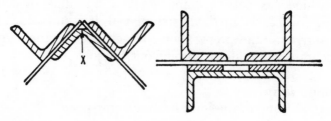

Fig. 25. Joint Fit-up Faults.

With close fitting joint, whole fillet (A) is effective, whereas with gap (B) weld metal is wasted, and only part (C) is effective for strength. With butt joint edges out of line, strength of joint is equal only to D (see Fig. 28).

or welding fixture. Straight joints may be set up with a tapered gap, as shown in Fig. 27, allowing the weld contraction to draw the edges together as the weld proceeds, the edges being kept in alignment by bolts and clamping plates or tongue and wedge clamps; alternatively, edges

Fig. 26.

Simple methods of clamping flat and corner sheet metal joints to maintain edge alignment and reduce distortion; to provide a gap under joint in corner joint, edge of angle should be removed, as at X.

may be set up with a small parallel gap and then tacked every few inches. Owing to the weakness of most non-ferrous metals at welding temperatures, a steel or copper

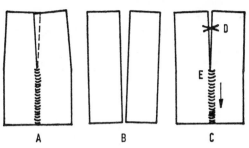

Fig. 27. Counteracting Weld Contraction on Long Joints.
A: Effect of weld contraction of free parallel joint. B: Taper-spacing allows for weld contraction. C: Weld partially completed; wedge at D maintains edge gap. Contraction also counteracted if weld is started at E and welded to end of joint, then remainder of joint welded – again starting at E.

back-up bar is often used under the joint to support the edges; the bar should be grooved under the joint to allow for penetration.

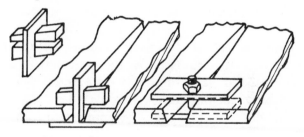

Fig. 28. Use of Clamps to Maintain Edge Alignment.

Good fit-up is also necessary for lap joints intended to be spot welded. Parts should be close fitting, with the surfaces meeting uniformly, otherwise unsatisfactory welds will result.

Controlling Distortion

Distortion due to fusion welding takes place in two directions, across and along the joint, and is particularly

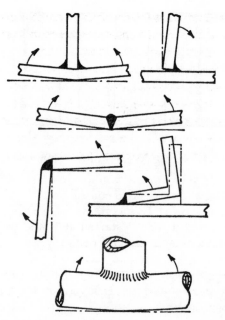

Fig. 29. Distortion Caused by Weld Contraction.

troublesome where long seams of complicated structures
are involved. It is caused by the contraction of the
deposited metal and the expansion and subsequent
contraction of the heated metal at the sides of the joint.
Weld metal contraction cannot be prevented (otherwise

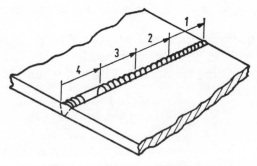

Fig. 30. Backstep Welding.

cracking may result), but it can be minimised by keeping the volume of the weld, i.e. its cross-section and length, as small as possible consistent with adequate strength and fusion of the joint. From then on distortion can only be controlled by restraining movement with clamps, presetting the parts before welding, using a step-back or skip technique to distribute the weld metal and welding

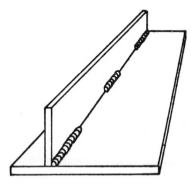

Fig. 31. Intermittent Welds.

heat as uniformly as possible over the joint, or by intermittent welding in order to minimise the total overall temperature rise of the weldment (see Fig. 31).

Distortion due to expansion of heated metal adjacent to the joint can only be reduced by minimising the area of heated metal, by absorbing the heat with copper bars clamped to the sides of the joint or by water cooling. Any technique that increases the welding speed, e.g. inert gas arc welding, also lessens the time during which the metal can absorb heat from the weld, resulting in less distortion.

Distortion is greatest with single-vee butt joints because the maximum contraction occurs on one face of the joint only; a double-bevelled joint welded equally from both sides minimises distortion by reducing the amount of weld metal required and equalising contraction on both faces of the joint.

Similarly, large single-tee fillets tend to create considerable contraction distortion, which can only be minimised by intermittent welds or by making small double fillets.

Each side of a joint should absorb the same amount of heat, otherwise the welder may find difficulty in maintaining both edges fusing equally, and unequal heat

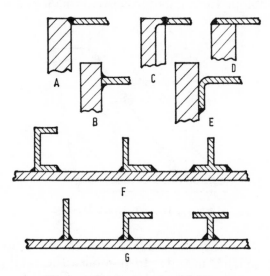

Fig. 32. Designing for Welding.

A & B: Bad types of joint for thick to thin components. C, D & E: Preferred types of thick to thin joints. F: Unsatisfactory ways of joining stiffeners to plate; more effective stiffeners and preferable types of welds are shown at G.

absorption results in unequal expansion, increased distortion or excessive fusion of the thinner component. Therefore, thick to thin welding is usually unsatisfactory, and whenever possible a thick edge should be reduced to the same thickness as the thinner edge (see Figs. 32 and 33). Where the heat absorption is very unbalanced, the balance may be adjusted by increasing the heat absorption of the thinner part with copper bars.

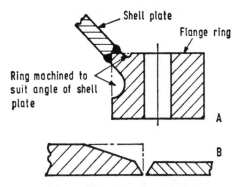

Fig. 33. Designing for Welding.

Thick components should be reduced in section to equalise
heat absorption of welding edges.

A: Joining dished end-plate to flange ring. B: Plate joint.

The presetting of joint components before welding (as
shown in Fig. 34) in order to allow the contraction to
bring the parts into the correct position is, of course,
limited to simple joints and cannot be applied to complicated weldments.

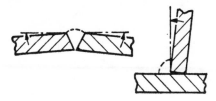

Fig. 34. Presetting Joints to allow for Weld Contraction.

Jigs, Manipulators and Positioners

The widest possible use should be made of jigs and clamping devices to facilitate downhand welding, minimise distortion and secure good welds, particularly for sheet
metal work and quantity production. Even for odd jobs
and small-quantity work, it is often not difficult to devise

simple jigs that will hold the welding edges firmly in place, and clamping in conjunction with chill bars will absorb much of the heat that would otherwise spread into the metal and cause distortion.

For mechanised welding of very thin sheet metal, accurate jigs are essential to ensure alignment of the welding edges so that neat, uniform welds may be made at the maximum speed possible with the process employed. This applies particularly to the use of the inert gas shielded arc processes in the fabrication of stainless steel and aluminium drums, pipes and other containers, and for joining sheets or strips where the very high welding speeds, in conjunction with a suitable jig, virtually eliminate distortion.

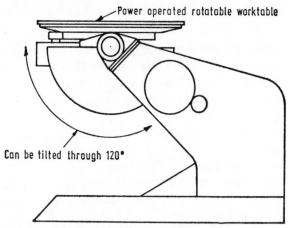

Fig. 35. A Typical Power-operated Positioner.

It enables all welds in a fabricated structure to be brought to the most convenient welding position.

(*F. Bode & Son Ltd.*)

Apart from one or two special procedures, downhand welding produces the best results and enables the highest welding speeds to be attained with the lowest cost. As far as possible, therefore, weldments should be positioned, or manipulated during welding to enable the greatest amount of welding to be done in the downhand position.

A wide selection of positioning equipment is available, ranging from hand-operated bench positioners for small assemblies to power-operated machines capable of manipulating workpieces weighing several tons. These positioners usually incorporate a rotating and tilting table, power-operated in the larger sizes, on which the workpiece is bolted; a convenient control arrangement enables any required movement to be obtained in order to bring the various joints into accessible and convenient welding positions.

For handling cylindrical workpieces, roller rotators are usually employed; these may be simple hand- or foot-operated machines, or they may be power-operated and capable of rotating workpieces weighing 100 tons or more. The latter are usually employed in conjunction with column- and boom-mounted submerged arc or continuous electrode welding heads to facilitate the welding of internal and external longitudinal and circumferential joints on pressure vessels and piping. Welding head rotators are also available for welding flanges, nozzles, bosses, etc., into boiler drums and other large weldments too cumbersome to be rotated.

Manipulating equipment is, of course, indispensable for the large fabrication shop, but even the small welding shop can often improvise or adapt pieces of machinery or rollers that will enable weldments to be manipulated to minimise positional welding; such equipment will usually well repay its cost in the increased production and greater economy obtained.

The Weldability of Metals

Weldability is a much-used word, obviously intended to describe the ease – or otherwise – with which a metal may be welded. Actually, there is no recognised method of classifying the weldability of the different metals – there are too many variables. However, it is possible to attempt a brief survey of those factors that affect the weldability (for the fusion welding processes) of the most commonly used metals, i.e. their thermal characteristics and their reactions to the application of welding heat.

Generally, the factors that decrease the weldability or increase the fusion welding difficulties of metals are:

1. Very high or very low heat conductivity.
2. High degree of expansion when heated (high thermal expansion).
3. Low strength when hot (hot shortness).
4. Cold brittleness (cold shortness).
5. Tendency to oxidise readily when hot.
6. Tendency for the weld to harden by air cooling or by the quench effect of surrounding cold metal.

With a metal having high thermal conductivity, e.g. copper, heat applied at the weld point is dissipated quickly into the remainder of the metal; this necessitates a large volume, or a more intense source, of welding heat or preheating to make up for the heat loss – hence the difficulty in spot welding copper. On the other hand, with a low thermal conductivity metal, e.g. stainless steel, the heat is concentrated in a narrow band along the joint; this may lead to overheating of the joint zone, and it restricts the area in which expansion can take place. Thus it is often desirable to use copper bars under or at the sides of the joint to assist in heat dispersal.

Metals with a high coefficient of thermal expansion, e.g. aluminium and copper, expand and contract more for a given heat input than those with a lower expansion coefficient, thus creating difficulties in counteracting distortion.

A metal that is 'hot short' has low strength at welding

| Metal | Melting point °C | Average tensile strength | | Approximate thermal properties compared with steel = 1 | | Electrical conductivity |
		tonf/-in²*	N/mm²	Heat conductivity ratio	Linear expansion ratio	Ratio compared with steel = 1
Mild steel	1500 (av.)	30–35	460–540	1	1	1
Heat- and corrosion-resisting steels	1420 (av.)	40	620	$\frac{1}{3}$	1½	1
Cast iron	1150–1200	6–13	93–200	1	1	—
Nickel alloys	1350–1450	36–45	550–700	$\frac{1}{3}$–1¼	1	1
Copper	1080	12–15	185–230	7	1½	3
Brass	900–950	8–20	120–310	2½	1½	2
Aluminium alloys	600 (av.)	8–25	120–390	3–4	2·0	4

Table 5. Factors Affecting the Weldability of Metals
(Comparative Thermal, Physical and Electrical Properties).

* 1 tonf/in² (ton force per square inch) = 15·44 N/mm² (newtons per millimetre squared).

temperatures, necessitating care to avoid contraction restraint and movement of parts during welding; small welds, such as tacks on cold metal, may crack when cooling. Cold shortness, on the other hand, indicates low strength at normal temperatures, e.g. cast iron; care is therefore necessary to minimise expansion at the weld point in order to avoid the creation of stresses at other points of the casting.

A metal that oxidises readily at welding temperatures, e.g. aluminium, is difficult to weld, due to the need to use a flux to minimise atmospheric contact with the molten metal and to eliminate or control any oxide formed. This is one reason why the inert gas arc processes improve the weldability of stainless steel and aluminium: the weld zone is completely protected from oxidation and no flux is required.

A tendency to harden by rapid cooling necessitates the use of preheat to remove the quench effect of cold metal and to reduce the cooling rate.

	Mild steel	Corrosion- and heat-resisting steels	Nickel alloys	Copper	Brass	Aluminium and Magnesium alloys
Mild Steel	E	F	F	P	P	—
Corrosion- and heat-resisting steels	F	E	G	P	P	—
Nickel alloys	F	G	E	P	P	—
Copper	P	P	P	P	P	—
Brass	P	P	P	F	F	—
Aluminium and magnesium alloys	P	—	—	—	—	F

E = Excellent   G = Good   F = Fair   P = Poor

Table 6. Spot Weldability of Metals.

For the spot, projection and seam welding processes, the electrical conductivity of a metal is an additional factor affecting its weldability. High conductivity (or low resistance) metals such as copper and aluminium allow the current to pass across the joint with less generation of heat than would be the case with, say, steel; hence the need for exceptionally high currents for these metals.

Metal Identification

A matter closely associated with the weldability of metals is the ability to identify a metal in order to know what type of treatment to apply. Some metals, such as steel, copper, aluminium and brass, are broadly recognisable by their colour and weight, but there are other metals and alloys that are difficult to identify in this way; it is, therefore, useful to be able to apply some simple tests that will assist in this identification.

Grinding Tests

For steels, sparking the metal on a grinding wheel is a simple and reliable test for type; all that is required is a grinder and some samples of mild, high carbon, manganese and other 'known' steels. These samples should be labelled and then sparked by holding them, one at a time, with a light, steady pressure against the grinding wheel, observing the spark pattern. An unknown piece of steel can then be sparked in the same way and identified by comparison. The general spark patterns will be as follows:

Low carbon (mild) steels: long, light yellow spark lines, slightly forked.
Medium carbon steels: similar to above, but the spark lines have secondary bursts with light yellow stars.
High carbon (tool) steels: spark lines shorter, with

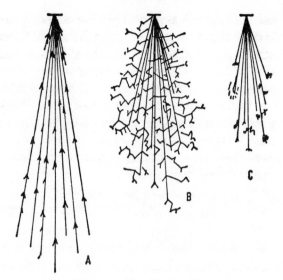

Fig. 36. Spark Testing.
A: Mild steel. B: Tool steel. C: Cast iron.

numerous light yellow stars; explosions with short, bushy clusters of sparks close to wheel.

Manganese steels: few bright, bushy sparks and light streaks may be sprayed round rim of wheel.

Stainless steels: practically no spark.

Malleable iron castings: moderate volume of sparks with fine repeating spurts; sparks are red close to wheel and straw-coloured at end of stream.

Grey cast iron: similar to above, but smaller volume of sparks.

In general, for iron and steel the higher the carbon, the denser and shorter the spark lines, and the greater the tendency for the sparks to burst.

Magnetic Tests
Most ordinary steels and irons are strongly magnetic and may be tested with a simple pocket magnet. On the other

hand, stainless steels and manganese steels are non-magnetic or only slightly magnetic. Straight chromium steel is strongly magnetic. (A further check of stainless steels may be made by dropping one or two drops of concentrated nitric acid on the metal; there will be no reaction if the metal is stainless steel. Care should be taken to make sure that the metal being tested is not a nickel or a stainless *clad* steel.)

Most non-ferrous metals (i.e. those containing no iron) are non-magnetic, except nickel, which is strongly magnetic, and Monel, which is sometimes slightly magnetic. Inconel and other nickel alloys, including some types of Monel, are non-magnetic.

The metal surface should be thoroughly cleaned and

Colour	Temperature	
	°C	°F
Brilliant white	1300	2350
White	1200	2200
Yellow-white	1100	2000
Orange-red	1000	1800
Bright cherry-red	850	1600
Cherry-red	750	1400
Dull cherry-red	650	1200
Dark red	600	1100
Faint red in twilight	500	950
Faint red in dark	400	750
Light straw	230	450

Table 7. Temperature Colours for Steel.

(Approximate temperatures indicated by the colour of steel when heated.*)

* The temperatures given in Celsius and Fahrenheit units are not necessarily exact equivalents, but are given to the nearest 50° for the sake of simplicity.

any surface coating or oxide skin removed before testing. To test accurately suspend the magnet and bring the specimen slowly to the magnet, noting carefully any slight movement of the magnet.

Other Tests

Light non-ferrous castings may be either aluminium or magnesium alloys. Magnesium alloy castings are much lighter than aluminium; new castings may have a golden colour due to a chromating treatment, but old castings are usually a dull grey colour. The metal may be tested by sprinkling on a few drops of sal ammoniac (ammonium chloride) mixed with water; the solution will bubble on magnesium alloy, but there will be no reaction if it is aluminium.

A file test is also useful. Aluminium filings clog the file, magnesium filings do not. Magnesium alloy filings will ignite if heated with an oxy-acetylene flame, while aluminium filings become black oxide.

Grey iron and malleable castings are easily chipped or drilled; malleable iron will produce chips that curl, whereas ordinary cast iron powders or produces very small chips. White iron is practically unmachinable.

Welding Steels

Mild steel forms the bulk of all welding applications. It is easy to weld because its ductility enables it to accommodate normal welding expansion and contraction without fracturing; also, it retains much of its strength when hot and is not particularly sensitive to welding conditions, i.e. it does not oxidise excessively or tend to harden when cooling and does not require a flux.

The term 'mild' steel indicates a steel containing less than 0·3% carbon; such steels are not hardenable by rapid cooling from welding temperatures. If the carbon content is higher than this, or if special alloying ingredients are used (see 'High Tensile Steels' page 79), difficulties may arise because of the tendency to hardening or cracking due to air cooling or the quench effect of the cold metal; in such cases preheating is desirable.

Manganese and stainless steels, iron, steel and some non-ferrous castings are hard to weld in that they are more sensitive to the effects produced by the intense, highly localised and often suddenly applied heat of welding, and to the contact of the atmosphere on molten metal.

It may be desirable to preheat to avoid sudden and localised heating of the metal, and slow cooling may be necessary to reduce and disperse stresses set up when the weld contracts.

Welding Processes
The processes already described in Part 1 are, according to the thickness to be welded, applicable to all types of mild steel welding.

Oxy-acetylene welding may be employed for sheet steel, but the widespread heat and low temperature of the oxy-acetylene flame is not suitable for thick steel welding. The highly localised heat of the arc enables higher welding speeds to be obtained with less heating of the metal at the sides of the joint and, therefore less distortion. With suitable joint preparation and multi-pass welding, any reasonable thickness may be arc welded either manually or with one of the special processes already described.

For manual welding there is a wide choice of electrodes. For low cost work, where the welding is mainly downhand a cheap electrode may be satisfactory; but when good-quality joints are important and position work is involved better-class electrodes are certainly desirable – and may actually be more economical to use due to ease of welding. Special electrodes are also avail-

Table 8. Approximate Weight of Deposit Metal (kg/m) Required for M.S. Joints.

Throat dimension (fillets) or plate thickness (butts)		90° Fillets*	Butt joints (downhand)				
in	mm		Square edges†	Single 60° vee	Double 60° vee	Single U	Double U
1/8	3	·08	·045				
3/16	5	·23	·09	·20			
1/4	6	·32	·133	·35			
5/16	8	·55	·213	·53			
3/8	10	·85	·36	·77	·28		
1/2	12	1·25	·54		·40		
3/4	20			2·13	1·10	2·40	1·90
1	25			3·30	1·70	3·30	1·90

* No gap   † Gap not exceeding ½ plate thickness.

Notes:

One cubic inch of steel weighs 0·28 lbs (0·127 kg) : one cubic cm weighs approx, 0·0081 kg.

The weights given above include normal surface reinforcement.

Vee angle and gap influence the amount of weld metal required (see Fig. 23).

able for pipe welding, high-speed downhand welding and deep penetration welding. Crack-resisting 'low hydrogen' electrodes should be used when welds are made on rigid joints, i.e. where weld metal contraction is liable to be restrained.

In the continuous electrode (wire) processes, bare wire is used with a protective gas or a powder flux, or the wire may incorporate a flux; such wires are extensively used for rebuilding worn parts or hard facing.

Resistance welding is applicable to almost all types of steel, and the spot, seam and projection welding processes are extensively used, particularly for sheet metal products. The flash welding process is employed for steel rail, pipe and section joining; also for joints in shaped sheet metal sections, such as automobile body components.

With these considerations as a background, mild steel is, therefore, a good metal for the beginner to start with, and instructions for welding other metals are frequently based on the accepted procedure for steel welding; moreover, pieces of steel scrap are usually readily available for inexpensive practice work.

However, it should be understood that, even with mild steel, there is a limit to its ductility, i.e. it may crack if suddenly chilled, and the molten metal in the weld pool should not be exposed to excessive atmospheric contamination by needless puddling or agitation.

*Learning to Weld**

Bearing these points in mind, a beginner can acquire some practical skill and experience in the behaviour of metals when heated and melted by making deposits on the surface of some pieces of scrap ¼ in [6 mm] steel plate. This will enable some ability to be acquired in depositing a straight bead, uniform in width and height; after

* See also page 163.

chipping and brushing away slag, the adequacy of the fusion between deposit and plate surface can be tested with a chisel or by bending the plate.

For arc welding, use a 10 gauge [3·25 mm] electrode and set the current regulator to about 125 A; adopt a comfortable position and, with the welding screen held in front of the eyes, practise striking an arc with the same motion as would be used for striking a match, holding the electrode at about 80° and starting with the electrode tip about $\frac{1}{2}$ in [12 mm] from the plate surface. When some ability in striking, and holding, the arc has been acquired, strike and hold an arc with the end of the electrode not more than $\frac{1}{16}-\frac{1}{8}$ in [1·6–3 mm] from the plate, and move the electrode steadily backwards in a straight line, thus depositing a bead of weld metal, as shown in Fig. 37.

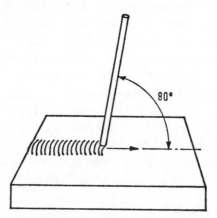

Fig. 37. Downhand Welding.

It will be necessary to regulate the speed so that there is neither too much nor insufficient fusion and, as shown in Fig. 38 (page 76), the bead is neither too narrow (speed too high) nor too heavily built up (speed too slow).

While welding, the electrode hand must be steadily

lowered to allow for the electrode burn-off and to maintain a constant arc length.

Later, set up two pieces of ⅜ in [10 mm] plate at about 70° in a jig, as shown at F in Fig. 38; if necessary, tack each end. Using a 10 s.w.g. [3·25 mm] electrode, weld the bottom of the vee; inspect for undercut at the sides of the weld and on the underside for penetration. Bend and break the joint (bottom of weld outwards) to inspect for fusion at the bottom of the weld.

Metal thickness		Electrode size		Amperage required
in	mm	s.w.g.	mm	A*
1/16	1·6	14	2	30–60
⅛	3	12	2·5	70–100
		10	3·25†	100–140
3/16	5	10	3·25†	100–140
¼–⅜	6–10	10	3·25†	100–140
		8	4	125–175
⅜–½	10–12	8	4	125–175
		6	5	180–260
½ and over		4	6	260–300

Table 9. Arc welding steel (downhand butt joints).

* Reduce by about 20% for vertical welding.
† The BS 4391 first choice metric equivalent for 10 s.w.g. is 3·25 mm.

With other pieces set up in the same way, make further welds, filling the vee. Tack pieces of plate together to form a tee and make single-fillet welds, first as shown at H, then as at G. Inspect all welds externally and by breaking, and correct faults by taking the appropriate action – correcting speed, electrode angle and arc length. Also notice the distortion created by the contraction of the deposit (see page 58). If practice in rebuilding worn surfaces or hard facing is desired, see page 143.

When good, sound welds can be obtained with uniform, but not excessive, penetration and build-up, plates may be set up for vertical corners fillets and horizontal,

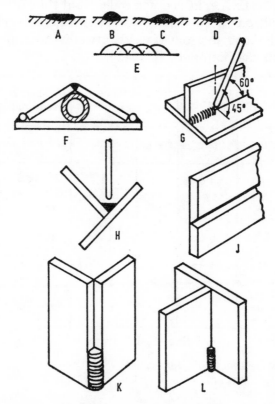

Fig. 38. Arc Welding Practice.

A: Welding bead too heavy with overlaps (current too high). B: Bead too narrow (speed too fast). C: Undercutting (excessive weave). D: Correct bead. E: When building up a surface, beads should overlap to avoid slag trapping. F: Jig for making downhand welds. G: Positional fillet welding. H: Downhand fillet weld. J: Vertical horizontal butt. K: Vertical corner weld. L: Vertical fillet.

vertical butts, as shown in Fig. 38. Practice should be made in depositing multi-runs, weaving to increase width of deposit or maintain two edges fusing, and small size runs with a very short arc.

Gas Welding

For the oxy-acetylene welder, the practice will be different in that this process is most likely to be used for sheet metals and for butt and corner joints only. The welder should therefore use pieces of thin (e.g. 10 or 12 gauge [3·25 or 2·5 mm] steel) plate to make practice beads, butt welds and corner joints (see Fig. 3, page 7).

Select a nozzle or tip suitable for the thickness to be welded and adjust the pressure regulators accordingly. Light the gases at the tip with the oxygen valve on the torch fully open and the acetylene valve partly open. Adjust the acetylene valve until the inner 'cone' in the

Metal thickness mm	Mild and stainless steels	
	Torch tip sizes*	
	Number	Litres
1·2	2	75
1·6	3	100
2·5	5	150
3·0	7	200
5·0	13	350

Flame adjustment: See page 82 for special reference to stainless steels

Table 10. Oxy-acetylene Welding Steels (downhand butt joints).

* In this and subsequent tables (Nos. 13, 15, and 17) the tip number indicates the consumption of each gas in cubic feet per hour. The litre figures are also for each gas per hour, but are not necessarily the equivalent of the tip numbers given.

flame is sharply outlined, i.e. without haziness or flicker. Finally, open the acetylene valve just a little more until a *slight* flicker appears at the end of the cone. This flame is neutral (see page 11) and is suitable for steel, stainless steel, aluminium, etc.; but as the tip becomes hot the flicker will disappear, and the acetylene valve must be adjusted occasionally to bring it back.

The torch should be held at 60–70° with the plate surface, and with the tip of the white cone just clear of the metal – no higher.

Tack the welding edges and make rightward and leftward runs (as in Fig. 7), without weaving, using $\frac{1}{16}$ in [1·6 mm] or $\frac{3}{32}$ in [2·5 mm] steel filler wire to acquire ability in securing uniform fusion and penetration; $\frac{3}{32}$ in [2·5 mm] welding wire should then be used to add weld metal, again practising to obtain uniform fusion and build up. Similar welds should then be made on thinner and thicker pieces of plate until full control over fusion, penetration and build-up of the weld surface has been acquired.

Non-fusion Welding

Steel components may be joined together or to other metals by using a bronze-type filler rod with oxy-acetylene welding. This is a non-fusion process since the steel is only heated sufficiently to enable the filler rod to 'tin' onto the steel surface – just as solder does on heated clean brass. The joint surface must be absolutely clean, sharp corners must be removed and a flux used to ensure efficient 'tinning'; generally, fillet or lap joints are more satisfactory than butt joints. As the bronze welding rods contain zinc, a slightly oxidising flame should be used to minimise zinc loss (see page 99).

Very neat, strong welds are obtainable, and there is less heat input and distortion than there would be with fusion welding. The process is also excellent for steel tubular structures, stainless steels (see page 81) and copper (see page 92), and for joining galvanised parts, since the welding temperature is not sufficient to destroy the galvanising. It is also used extensively for repairing cast and malleable iron castings, and rebuilding worn parts (see page 130), and dissimilar metals may be jointed, e.g. copper to steel and steel to cast iron.

High Tensile Steels

For those types of construction or machinery requiring steel having more strength than that normally provided by mild steel, high tensile steels are employed. These steels are not as easily welded as mild steel, since – unless precautions are taken – there may be a tendency to hardening and cracking in the weld zone; otherwise, provided the appropriate size and type of electrodes are used, the welding processes for these steels are similar to those for mild steel, except that preheat may be needed. Particular attention should be paid to the mechanical quality of the welding, avoiding undercutting, craters and roughness of the weld surface which may create a notching effect and encourage cracking. A 'low hydrogen' electrode should be used.

Clad Steels

For chemical and other plant subject to corrosive conditions, the use of a relatively low-cost steel base coated or clad with a corrosion-resisting metal, such as stainless steel, copper or nickel alloy, provides an economical method of construction, and the joining of these steels is an interesting welding application.

Arc welding is the most commonly employed method of joining both the steel and the cladding, although the inert gas arc processes have been applied to the cladding and the submerged arc to the steel base.

Although it is possible to make the entire weld with the electrode used for the cladding, particularly for stainless clad steels, it is more usual to treat the steel base and the cladding separately, making two welds, each with a different electrode, otherwise the corrosion resistance of

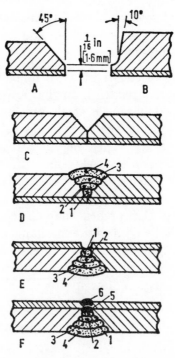

Fig. 39. The Preparation and Welding of Clad Steels.*

A: Preparation of plate $\frac{3}{16}$ in [5 mm] to $\frac{5}{8}$ in [16 mm] thick.
B: Preparation of plate above $\frac{5}{8}$ in [16 mm] thick. The small edge of steel above the cladding protects the cladding during welding from steel side. C: Alignment of plates. D: Welding of the steel side with a steel electrode. Note that the weld metal has not penetrated the cladding. E: Clad side prepared for welding by grinding or chipping. F: Two passes have been made on the clad side to complete the joint.

* From *Welding of Clad Steels*. (The International Nickel Co. Ltd.)

the cladding weld may be impaired due to dilution from the steel base.

It is important to maintain the continuity of the cladding; therefore, butt welds (see Fig. 39) are preferred and accurate alignment of the edges is essential. Edges may be prepared by machining or gas cutting (from the steel side); metal arc oxy-cutting using a hollow electrode may also be employed, but machining or grinding is usually necessary to smooth the edge.

Joints should preferably be welded downhand, welding the steel side first; when the steel side is completed, the clad side must be chipped down to clean weld metal, with a groove wide enough to permit access to the root, and on all but the thinnest material the cladding weld should be made in two runs to ensure a surface with the minimum dilution.

When fillet and corner joints are unavoidable, the same basic principles should be observed to secure joint strength and continuity of the cladding.

Corrosion- and Heat-resisting Steels

As will be seen from Table 5 on page 65, the thermal characteristics of these steels – generally known as stainless steels – differ considerably from those of ordinary steels; their expansion is about 50% greater, their heat conductivity about 50% less and their melting point slightly lower.

The alloying elements – principally nickel and chromium – which give the metal its corrosion-resisting properties, also make the metal very sensitive to heat effects, necessitating care in the application of welding.

Some alloys are unweldable, due to the risk of air hardening, weld cracking and reduction of corrosion resistance in the weld zone, but fortunately the most commonly used type, known as 18/8 (containing 18%

chromium and 8% nickel), is also the most readily weldable. For welded products it is, therefore, necessary to use only those types known to be suitable for welding.

The thermal characteristics of the metal tend to concentrate the heat effects into a narrow zone along the weld. Excessive buckling, and perhaps cracking, may therefore result if weld zone movement is restrained; this can be minimised by absorbing some heat into copper bars clamped on each side of the joint over a copper back-up bar. Flame preheating of the weld area is sometimes used to lessen the heat concentration in the weld zone.

Gas Welding
Use a non-oxidising flame, with the end of the cone showing a very slight flicker. As welding proceeds, the flame tends to become oxidising and will need frequent readjustment; if an oxidising flame is used, the weld will probably be unsound. On the other hand, if the flame is appreciably carbonising, the corrosion resistance and ductility of the weld will be affected. A smaller tip than would normally be employed for mild steel should be used, or the gas pressures may be reduced to give a similar effect, since a soft flame ensuring tranquil fusion is essential – particularly on thin sheet, where there may be a danger of piercing the metal if the gas pressures are too high.

Close tacking of the joint is necessary to maintain edge alignment, and the weld should be completed as quickly as possible to minimise distortion.

The welding wire should be of the same type of steel as that being welded and the same size as, or slightly larger than, the gauge of steel. The tip of the white cone should be kept in contact with the molten metal, and the filler wire should be fed into the joint continuously, not intermittently. A flux, mixed with water to a creamy paste, should be applied to the underside of the joint and to the feed wire; after welding, any flux residue must be removed by immersing the parts in a boiling 5% caustic soda solution.

Arc Welding

For arc welding, either a.c. or d.c. (electrode positive) may be used; rectified a.c. gives a steady arc suitable for light gauge welding. Two types of electrodes are available: with a mild steel core wire and with a stainless core wire. The mild steel core wire* electrodes have a number of advantages over the conventional types: they strike and weld more easily, deposit more metal per electrode length and weld faster, and are therefore excellent for downhand butt welds. The stainless core electrodes deposit less slag and may therefore be preferred by some welders for fillet and position welding.

Apart from stainless steels which are used for their non-rusting and corrosion-resisting properties, there are a number of high chromium, high nickel alloys used for applications requiring exceptional heat resistance, e.g. case hardening and annealing boxes which are weldable.

It is most important to use the correct class of electrode for the type of steel being welded; electrodes are available for all the weldable alloys. Dry electrodes are essential, as dampness may cause weld porosity and possible cracking; therefore, they should be kept in a warm, dry store, or should be warmed immediately before use (an ordinary domestic electric oven can be used for this purpose). Electrodes with damaged coatings should not be used, as the analysis and soundness of the deposit may be adversely affected.

The current setting should be lower than for steel, and the arc should be as short as possible, since a long arc often results in unsound welds, lack of penetration and loss of alloying elements. Weaving must be avoided, and

* Stainless ingredients in the coating.

Metal thickness		Electrode sizes		Current range A*	Type of joint
in	mm	s.w.g.	mm		
(20 s.w.g.)	1	16	1·6	20–25	Sq. edge
$\frac{1}{16}$	1·6	14	2	40–50	,, ,,
$\frac{1}{8}$	3	12	2·5	70–90	,, ,,
$\frac{3}{16}$	5	10	3·25	90–110	Sq. edge or 60° vee
$\frac{1}{4}$	6	8	4	110–140	60° vee
$\frac{3}{8}$ and over	10 and over	8 and/or 10 (multi-run welds)	3·25–4 (multi-run welds)	As above	,, ,,

Table 11. Arc Welding Stainless Steel (downhand butt joints).

* Reduce by 10% for vertical welding.

at the end of each electrode run the arc should be drawn back along the weld bead and the electrode lifted slowly in order to eliminate crater cavities.

In general, joint edges should be prepared as for mild steel welding. A good joint fit-up is desirable and, unless jigs are used, edges should be tacked every few inches; for example, on $\frac{3}{16}$ in [5 mm] thick plate, tacks should be spaced 6–8 in [150–200 mm] apart, but spacing down to 2 in [50 mm] apart should be used on thinner metal. All tacks should be scratch-brushed before making the weld. Weld on a clean bench and use stainless steel wire brushes for cleaning joint edges and welds.

With multiple-run welds, it is essential to chip and scratch-brush each run before starting the next in order to remove all slag and oxide which, in subsequent contact with corrosive media, may turn into rust. Discolouration due to welding may be removed either by using one of the preparations sold for the purpose or by grinding and polishing.

Inert Gas Arc Welding

For large-scale production, the inert gas process (MIG welding), applied manually or by machine, is superior to gas or arc welding. Special equipment and techniques have been developed for the making of butt welds by machine welding in metal as thin as 0·005 in [0·12 mm], and at speeds of up to 50 in [1·27 m] per minute. Very low currents are employed; for 20 s.w.g. [1 mm] sheet, a current of 30 to 40 A is sufficient, and it is essential that the generator or other power source should be capable of giving a steady arc at this low current. Very high speeds with very little distortion are readily obtainable.

Resistance Welding

Since stainless steels have high electrical resistivity and low thermal conductivity, which retards the dissipation of heat into the surrounding metal, it is necessary to use a lower current setting than would be employed for mild steel of the same gauge. Otherwise, the 18/8 stainless steels are ideal for spot, projection spot, stitch and seam welding, but certain essential operating conditions are necessary. Spot welding machines must be sufficiently rigid to enable more pressure than would be necessary for mild steel to be exerted by the electrodes; if the arms are not rigid, sideways movement of one electrode in relation to the other will cause an unsound weld. Special hard copper alloy electrodes are required – plain copper is too soft.

By using a larger electrode on one arm, the weld depression on that side of the joint can be eliminated; this feature is particularly useful in the fabrication of domestic utensils. The use of a high current for an accurately controlled short period is preferable to a smaller current for a longer period. With the former condition, a properly fused weld nugget can be obtained without discolouring or marking the surface of the metal.

Non-fusion Welding

As with ordinary steels, stainless steel components not intended for high temperatures or corrosive conditions may be joined without fusion by using oxy-acetylene bronze welding. Heat input and distortion is thereby reduced, and detrimental heat effects on the metal are minimised. It is, however, desirable to match as far as possible the corrosion resistance of the steel, and a high nickel type of bronze filler rod must therefore be used. A stainless steel bronze welding flux should also be used.

The process is excellent for fillet welds and may also be used for butt joints in sheet metal; but, since bronze welding is a surface application, the deposited metal must be left as welded, i.e. butt joints cannot be ground flush. Alternatively, the weld may be made from the back.

Nickel and Nickel Alloys*

Nickel, Monel, Inconel and other nickel alloys are extensively used for acid and heat corrosion-resisting applications, in the chemical, food, oil and gas turbine industries. Most of the alloys are not difficult to weld, the procedures being generally similar to those employed for steel, the choice of process – fusion or resistance welding – depending on the availability of the equipment and the requirements of the weld. These metals are not particularly critical in their welding requirements, but, when hot, they are extremely sensitive to contamination by any sulphur perhaps present in surface coatings or markings, on the welding bench or in gas flames which might be used for preheating. Before welding absolute cleanliness of the surfaces adjacent to the welding edges and avoidance of any sulphur-containing lubricants, paints or gases is, therefore, important, and any machining of welding edges should be done dry.

* Manufacturers' welding literature should be obtained (see page 171).

Metal	Melting range °C	Thermal properties		Approx electrical conductivity ratio
		Heat conductivity ratio	Expansion ratio	
		Compared with steel = 1		
Nickel	1435–1445	$1\frac{1}{4}$	1	1
MONEL	1300–1350	$\frac{1}{2}$	1	$\frac{1}{5}$
INCONEL	1395–1425	$\frac{1}{3}$	1	$\frac{1}{10}$
NIMONIC (series)*	1320–1420	$\frac{1}{4}$	1	$\frac{1}{10}$

Table 12. Properties of Nickel Alloys.

* Not recommended for oxy-acetylene or arc welding; all nickel alloys are suitable for spot welding.

Metal thickness mm	Torch tip sizes			
	MONEL		NICKEL 200 INCONEL 600	
	Number	Litres	Number	Litres
·8	2–3	75/100	2	75
1·6	3–5	100/150	3	100
2·5	5–7	150/200	5	150
3·0	7–10	200/300	7	200
5·0	10–13	300/350	10	300
Flame adjustment	Very slightly carbonising		Neutral	

Table 13. Oxy-acetylene welding should only be used where facilities are limited or for on-site welding (downhand butt joints).

Butt joints should be used whenever possible with jigs or clamps to maintain the alignment of the welding edges, avoiding the use of tacks; edge preparations are shown in Fig. 40.

Arc Welding

D.c. is necessary with electrode positive. Weld as for mild steel using a short arc with the electrode held 20° from vertical, pointing towards the completed weld; a long arc, excessive amperage or wrong polarity will cause spatter. As much welding as possible should be carried out down-hand, and it is an advantage to incline the work surface slightly so that the weld is made uphill. Electrodes must be dried before using.

Metal thickness		Electrode diam.		Current range A*			Type of joint
in	mm	s.w.g.	mm	MONEL†	Nickel†	INCONEL†	
⅛–³⁄₁₆	3–5	10	3·25	60–95	95–120	80–100	Sq. edge or 75° vee
¼	6	8	4	80–150	120–160	110–130	75° vee
⅜–½	10–12	6	5	140–190	170–200	130–150	75° vee

Table 14. Arc Welding Nickel Alloys.

* D.C. electrode positive.
† Appropriate electrodes must be used.

The welding slag created by arc welding is difficult to remove and entrapment must be avoided by careful control during welding; any surface slag must be removed immediately after welding by wire brushing, particularly for parts intended for heat treatment or high temperature service, as slag left on the metal is liable to cause corrosion.

To minimise the risk of slag trapping care is necessary

when breaking the arc to avoid the formation of craters, and multi-pass welding should be avoided. Single beads should be deposited as far as possible without weaving; any weave necessary on thick plate should not exceed three times the core wire diameter.

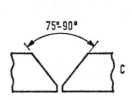

Fig. 40. Edge Preparations for Nickel Alloys.

A. For up to 18 s.w.g. (1·2 mm).
B. For thicknesses up to $\frac{1}{8}$ in (3 mm).
C. 80° V for $\frac{3}{16}$ in (5 mm) to $\frac{3}{8}$ in (10 mm). Use double 80° Vee preparation for $\frac{1}{2}$ in (12 mm) and over.
D. Alternative for over $\frac{1}{2}$ in (12 mm).

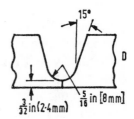

Inert Gas Arc Welding

The MIG and TIG processes can be used for nickel and almost all the alloys, giving welds of excellent quality provided the joint is correctly prepared and the inert gas flow and the welding current are correctly adjusted. Use a short arc and avoid dilution of the shielding gas and puddling of the weld, otherwise the quality of the weld may be detrimentally affected. Weld away from draughts and hold the torch at 90° as close as possible to the work surface. With TIG welding direct current is preferable and TIG welding wires should be used – not oxy-acetylene welding wires.

Gas Welding

The welding tip should be slightly larger than for a similar thickness of steel, with a soft, slightly carbonising flame, i.e. with a slight flicker of the inner cone. Avoid a strongly carbonising flame, as Inconel alloys, in particular, are detrimentally affected by too much acetylene. Mix flux (not needed for nickel) to a thin paste and paint on both sides of the joint and the filler wire. General procedure is similar to that for steel, avoiding puddling or agitation of the molten metal with the flame or welding wire. Keep the tip of the cone just touching the weld pool, with the end of the wire in the pool or within the flame to avoid oxidation. Unused and fused flux must be removed immediately after welding by hot water washing and wire brushing.

Resistance Welding

All the resistance welding processes can be applied to the jointing of the high nickel alloys. The same precautions previously mentioned concerning cleanliness of surfaces, particularly with regard to the avoidance of sulphur contamination, should be observed, and any oxide film on the joint surfaces should be removed. Experiment may be required to ascertain the correct combination of electrode pressure, current setting and weld time to give the best results without sticking or excessive indentation.

Generally, the electrode pressures and the current settings will be somewhat higher, and the weld time shorter, than those used for a similar thickness of steel.

Water cooling of the work is recommended in order to minimise distortion and electrode pick-up.

Vessel Linings

Nickel, Monel and Inconel alloys are used extensively for

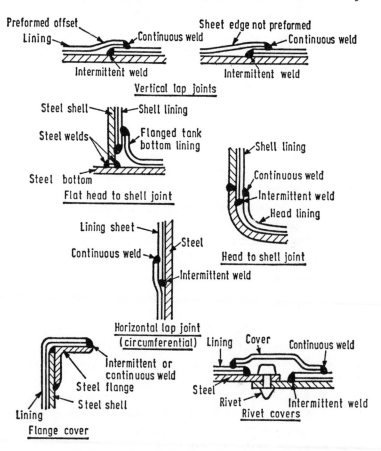

Fig. 41. Details of Nickel Alloy Vessel Lining Joints.*

* From *Welding, Brazing and Soldering of High Nickel Alloys*
(Henry Wiggin & Co. Ltd.).

lining steel and other metal vessels in order to provide a
corrosion-resisting interior surface. Most linings are
installed as strips 3–12 in [75–300 mm] wide, 16–14
s.w.g. [1·6–2 mm]. The various pieces must be accurately
shaped to follow the interior shape of the vessel, after
which they are degreased, jacked into position and joined
by metal arc welding, using the appropriate electrode

for the lining metal. Good fitting between the pieces is essential for satisfactory and economical welding; absolute cleanliness of the interior of the vessel is also important so as to avoid contamination of the back of the lining or the welded joints.

Copper and Copper Alloys*

Fusion welding by the inert gas shielded arc processes now supersedes all previously used processes therefore the welding details given (Tables 15 and 16) apply only to these processes.

Argon is the most commonly used shielding gas for both copper and its alloys but helium or nitrogen, either alone or mixed with argon, may be used for copper to increase the heat output of the arc and thus reduce the temperature of any preheat required and increase the penetration and welding rate. Welds made with nitrogen alone or mixed with argon, have a rough appearance but the weld itself is usually sound.

For MIG welding copper the details given apply only to argon but helium or nitrogen can be used as above to increase the heat output from the torch. However nitrogen mixed with argon destroys the normal spray transfer condition, but up to 50% helium mixed with argon tends to improve the arc behaviour and increase the heat input without destroying spray transfer. The high cost of helium may, therefore, be offset by improved welding performance.

Joint Preparation

Butt joint preparations are shown in Figs. 42 and 43.

* Recommended Institutional reading: *Fusion Welding and Brazing of Copper and Copper Alloys*, R. J. C. Dawson, (Newnes–Butterworth Press).

A 16 mm colour film *Inert Gas Arc Welding of Copper* is available on free loan from the C.D.A.

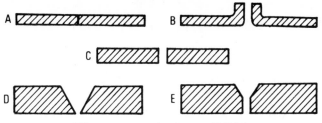

Fig. 42.   1.5 to 6 mm thick*

Number of runs: A, B, C, (1.5 mm) – one D and E (6 mm) –
one or two.

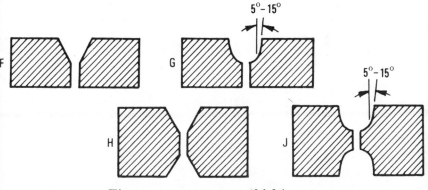

Fig. 43.   12 to 24 mm thick*

Preparation of Joint Edges for Copper Welding

* From Welding of Copper and Copper Alloys (Copper Development Association).

All joint edges and adjacent metal must be clean: use a
bronze wire brush to remove oxide and dirt, degrease with
petroleum, ether or alcohol. During multi-run welding brush
each run to remove oxide before proceeding.
All Vees should be 60° to 90°; root gap 1.5 mm; root face
1.5 tp 3 mm according to thickness.
Number of runs: F and G (12 mm) – two to four. F and G
(18 mm) – four to eight. H and J (24 mm and over) – ten or
more.

(A) TIG Welding (Direct current; electrode negative; argon, helium and nitrogen shielding)

Thickness (mm)	Electrode (mm)	Filler (mm)	Gas nozzle (mm)	Shielding gas					
				Argon		Nitrogen		Helium	
				Current (A)	Gas flow	Current (A)	Gas flow	Current (A)	Gas flow
1·5	1·6–2·4	1·6	9·5	80–130	4–6	—	—	70–90	6–10
3	2·4–3·2	1·6	9·5–12	120–240	4–6	—	—	180–220	6–10
6	3·2–4·8	3·2	12–18	220–350	6–8	220–260	12–16	200–240	10–15
12	4·8	3·2–4·8	12–18	330–420	8–10	240–280	14–20	260–280	10–15

Preheating needed for 6 mm and over. Gas flow in litres/minute.

(B) MIG Welding (1·6 mm diameter filler wire using Argon or Argon/Helium shielding)

Thickness (mm)	Welding current (A)	Arc voltage (V)	Wire feed rate (m/min)	Gas flow
6	240–320	25–28	6·5–8·0	10–15
12	320–380	26–30		10–15
18	340–400	28–32	5·5–6·5	12–17
24 and up	340–420	28–32		14–20

Preheating needed for 12 mm and over.

Table 15. Typical Operating Data for TIG and MIG Butt Welds in Copper

(A) Silicon Bronze: MIG – using 1·6 mm filler wire, feed rate 6·0–8·5 m/min, with argon. No preheat.

Thickness m/m	TIG				MIG		
	filler rod m/m	Gas nozzle m/m	Gas flow lit/min	A (amps)	V (Volts)	Gas flow lit/min	A (amps)
1·5	1·6	9·5/12	5–8	100/130	—	—	—
3·0	2·4	9·5/12	5–8	120/160	—	—	—
6·0	3·2			200/300	22–26	9–14	250–320
9·0	3·2–4·8	12–18	8–10	250/300	22–26	9–14	300–330
12·0	3·2–4·8			270/330	24–28	14–20	300–330
over 12·0	—	—	—	—	26–28	14–20	330–400

(B) Aluminium Bronze: MIG – using 1·6 mm filler wire, Argon, arc voltage 26–28 preheat if considered necessary, not to exceed 150° C.

Thickness m/m	TIG				MIG		
	Filler rod m/m	Gas nozzle m/m	Gas flow lit/min	A (amps)	Wire feed	Gas flow lit/min	A (amps)
1·5	1·6	9·5–12	5–8	100/130	—	—	—
3·0	3·2	9·5–12	5–8	180/220	—	—	—
6·0	3·2			280/320	4·5/5·5	9–12	280/300
9·0	3·2–4·8	12–15	8–10	360/420	5·5–6·0	9–12	300/330
12·0	3·2–4·8			360/420			320–3
18·0	—	—	—	—	5·8–6·2	12–17	320–35
24·0	—	—	—	—			340–40
24 up	—	—	—	—			360–42

TIG requirements for A and B: 3·2 mm electrodes, A.C. Argon shielding.

Table 16. MIG and TIG Welding Details for Copper-Based Alloys

Use suitable jigs and backing arrangements to align the joint edges, minimise distortion and control the weld bead; the design of such jigs etc. will, of course, depend upon the preheat requirements, metal thickness and type of joint.

If the underside of the joint is accessible, control penetration with a grooved mild or stainless steel backing bar coated with colloidal graphite or anti-spatter compound. Ceramic strip can be used with a backing bar to ensure a smooth, flush penetration and minimise heat dissipation.

If accessibility is restricted integral backing bars of a matching composition can be used to fuse into the weld and become an integral part of the joint.

Tacking may also be used to maintain alignment and root gap, but tacks must be made with the correct filler metal, preheat temperature etc., and must be wire brushed before welding to ensure efficient fusion with the first weld run.

Moveable clamps, as shown in Fig. 28, may also be used on long joints, moving the clamp along the joint as the weld progresses.

Preheating

For copper, preheating becomes increasingly important as the thickness increases, otherwise it is difficult to maintain a fluid weld pool with the arc heat alone.

For TIG welding, preheat when the thickness exceeds 3 mm with a maximum of 400° C for 6 mm, and 400 to 600° C for 12 mm; as previously mentioned, the preheat temperature can be considerably reduced when nitrogen or helium are used, due to the increased heat output from the arc. For MIG welding preheating is necessary for thicknesses over 6 mm, with maximum temperatures of 500° C for 12/18 mm and up to 700° C for 24 mm and over. Since copper alloys lose their ductility from 400°

upwards they should not be preheated, in fact, it is essential to avoid unnecessary heating of the joint, and multi-run temperature build-up should be minimised by allowing a cooling period after each run. If there are reasons why some preheat appears necessary, the maximum temperature should not exceed 150° C.

Resistance Welding

Copper is practicably unweldable by spot and seam welding because it tends to weld to the electrodes, the contact resistance being higher than the resistance between the work surfaces; in addition, the heat input is rapidly dissipated from the joint.

Phosphor bronzes (copper tin alloys) are also difficult to weld because the phosphorous content fluxes the surfaces in contact with the electrodes, causing sticking; this scars the work surfaces and necessitates frequent dressing of the electrodes. The red brasses (high copper, low zinc alloys) are also difficult to weld, but Everdur (silicon zinc alloy) and the yellow brasses are readily weldable.

With the weldable alloys, high currents are generally necessary in order to minimise 'weld' time, otherwise the heat will be dissipated too rapidly, and synchronous timing is desirable for consistent results.

The electrode pressures required are generally lower than those needed for ferrous metals, and the correct pressure to apply in any particular case should be established by test. For example, the machine may be set to deliver a somewhat higher current than the work is expected to require, with the electrode pressure also high; the electrode pressure can then be reduced until satisfactory welds are produced. The current setting can then also be reduced gradually and the process repeated until welds of the required size and quality are made with the least current and lowest electrode pressure.

Tips must be kept in good condition and frequently re-shaped by machining – not filing, which roughens the tip and accelerates depreciation.

Bronze Welding of Copper

This is an oxy-acetylene non-fusion downhand procedure using a bronze, i.e. a 60/40 brass alloy, filler rod; the copper is not melted but heated only sufficiently to 'tin' the joint edges with the filler rod (see page 78). Much less heat is put into the metal than would be the case with normal fusion welding; consequently, there is less distortion and the type of copper does not matter.

The flame should be slightly oxidising in order to minimise zinc loss from the filler rod, and a flux is needed. The joint edges may be butted or lapped. If the edges are square butted, a gap equal to half the metal thickness is required to ensure penetration of the weld metal; above $\frac{1}{8}$ in [3 mm] thick, the edges should be bevelled to provide a 60°–90° vee.

To make a joint the metal should be heated with the flame until the bronze filler rod melts or 'tins' when touched on the joint surface. The weld may then be made by 'tinning' the jointing surfaces and melting in enough bronze to form a joint. The flame heat should be directed

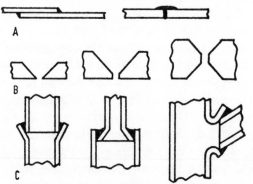

Fig. 44. Joints for the Bronze Welding of Copper.
A: Copper Sheet. B: Plate. C: Pipe.

partly on the rod and partly on the joint, so that the wetting or 'tinning' proceeds just ahead of the deposited metal. The molten metal is easier to control if the joint is inclined slightly and the weld made uphill.

Brass

Although inert gas welding is generally employed for 60/40 copper-zinc brasses, it is possible to use oxy-acetylene if inert gas equipment is not available. The chief welding difficulty with this process lies in the tendency to burn out the zinc, causing porosity and loss of strength. This can, however, be minimised by using an oxidising flame; the amount of excess oxygen required can be determined by melting a piece of scrap, starting with a slightly oxidising flame and gradually decreasing the acetylene until fuming ceases and no porosity is visible in the solidified melt.

Edge preparation for sheets is essentially the same as for copper, and before welding care should be taken to ensure correct edge alignment and adequate support of the joint components, as fracture may occur if the job is moved when the metal is hot. Metal over $\frac{1}{8}$ in [3 mm] thick must be bevelled, otherwise the application of excessive heat to secure penetration may cause collapse of the joint.

Flux should be applied to the top and undersides of the joint and welding wire; preheat to dark red and weld, without weaving, with the inner cone close to the surface, keeping the welding wire in the molten pool until the weld is finished.

If arc welding is employed, tin/bronze electrodes should be used with high current, and the arc should be kept on the weld pool without weaving. For inert gas TIG welding, use aluminium bronze filler alloy to reduce zinc fuming.

Spot and seam resistance welding is satisfactory, but electrode tips need to be kept in good condition and must be remachined (not filed) frequently.

Aluminium and Aluminium Alloys

Aluminium is fast becoming one of the most extensively used industrial metals; it has even superseded steel for some types of structural work, and its use for sheet metal work exceeds that of other sheet metals. The success that has attended the welding developments of the metal, despite several outstanding welding difficulties, now enables almost any type of welded fabrication to be produced by gas, arc or inert gas arc welding, preferably the latter.

The welding difficulties involved are the very low melting point, high rate of heat conductivity (up to five times that of steel) and high expansion rate; in addition, there is no change of colour to indicate when melting temperatures are approached, and many of the alloys are hot short and have very little strength at high temperatures.

Moreover, aluminium and aluminium alloys tend to oxidise very rapidly at welding temperatures, necessitating (for gas or arc welding) the use of a very active – and

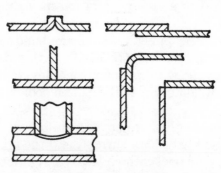

Fig. 45. Types of Joints not suitable for Gas and Arc Welding Aluminium due to risk of Flux Trapping.

corrosive – flux that will dissolve the oxide. The necessity for a corrosive flux is one of the disadvantages of the gas and arc processes – a disadvantage eliminated in the inert gas arc and resistance processes, which do not require a flux.

The low strength and hot shortness of some of the alloys at welding temperatures necessitate careful temperature control and support for the joint edges up to the weld point. Contraction restraint must be avoided, otherwise weld cracks may occur, and tacking should be done after preheating, for the chill of the cold metal and the sudden contraction of the deposit may also cause cracking.

Gas Welding
Oxy-acetylene welding may be employed for welding aluminium up to $\frac{3}{16}$ in [5 mm] thick, the flexibility of the

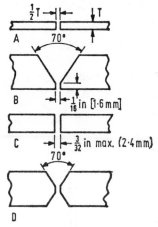

Fig. 46. Preparation of Aluminium Joint Edges for Gas Welding.

A: For downhand welding up to $\frac{3}{32}$ in [2·5 mm]. B: For downhand welding $\frac{3}{32}$ in–$\frac{3}{8}$ in [2·5 mm–10 mm]. C: For vertical (two-operator) welding up to $\frac{1}{4}$ in [6 mm]. D: For vertical welding over $\frac{1}{4}$ in [6 mm].

process and simplicity of the equipment being advantageous for small-scale production and work where accurate set-up or jigging of the joints is not possible or economical; for this reason also, the process is largely used for repair work. The main limitations of the process are the distortion caused by the rapid conduction of heat away from the weld point and the corrosive nature of the flux that must be employed. Absolute cleanliness of the metal surface is essential, and washing with a detergent is often desirable.

The tip should be a size larger than that used for steel of similar thickness, and the flame should be soft and neutral; any tendency to use a very small tip should be

Metal thickness	Torch tip sizes*		Type of joint (butt)
mm	Number	Litres	
1·6	3–5	100/150	Square edge
2·5	5–7	150/200	,, ,,
3	7–10	200/300	70° vee
4	10–13	300/400	,,
5	13–18	400/500	,,
Flame adjustment – neutral to slightly carbonising			

Table 17. Oxy-acetylene Welding Aluminium (downhand).

* Reduce gas pressures to ensure soft flame.

avoided, as too small a flame makes starting difficult, reduces the welding speed and makes the weld pool too small for adequate fusion.

Forward welding should be used, with the flame inclined at about 45°. As the weld advances and the metal becomes hot, the welding rate should increase and the flame angle should be decreased to reduce heat input;

any inclination to weave or lift the flame to avoid over-heating the joint or reduce the welding speed should be avoided, as this widens the heated zone, increasing oxidation and the danger of collapse.

The addition of silicon to aluminium lowers its melting point, and silicon-aluminium welding wires are therefore usually employed. Since the flux is corrosive and should be used sparingly, it may be mixed to a thin paste with alcohol and painted on the joint edges and welding wire; an alternative method is to dip the heated end of the wire into the flux and then melt down 'he adhering 'tuft' so that it varnishes the wire. Severa wires may be painted or coated before starting to weld; extra flux may be needed at the start of a weld, but the fluxed wire will be sufficient for welding.

*Arc Welding (d.c.)**

Joint edges should be absolutely clean and scratch-brushed immediately before welding. A copper backing bar may be used to support the edges and to control penetration.

Use silicon-aluminium electrodes, and keep them warm and dry†. The electrode should be held within 20° of the vertical, keeping the arc as short as possible, and movement should be in a straight line along the seam without weaving. Even for thick sections, the electrode should be moved only back and forth along the seam, maintaining a steady forward motion.

The welding speed is about three times faster than for mild steel and should be increased as the weld progresses. If the speed is high, or the current too low for the speed,

* A.c. to d.c. convertors are available for fitting to a.c. transformer-type welding plants so that the a.c. plant can be used for welding non-ferrous metals.

† Special electrodes for resisting sea-water corrosion are also available.

Metal thickness		Electrode size		Current range A	Type of joint (butt)
in	mm	s.w.g.	mm		
$\frac{1}{16}$	1·6	12	2·5	40–55	Close butt
$\frac{3}{32}-\frac{1}{8}$	2·5–3	10	3·25	65–75	Close butt
$\frac{3}{16}$	5	8	4	100–145	Butt with $\frac{1}{16}$ in [1·6 mm] gap
$\frac{1}{4}$	6	6	5	145–190	Butt with $\frac{1}{8}$ in (3·2 mm) gap
$\frac{3}{8}$	10	6	5	190–230	70° vee

Table 18. Arc Welding Aluminium (downhand).

The most effective current value should be found by trial; it is possible to use much higher currents on cold metal; moreover, the welding speed will be greater with higher currents.

the joint will be only partly welded; large electrodes and high currents give the best results.

Thick plates should be preheated (before tacking) to facilitate the production of a smooth weld, and electrodes should be heated and dried before use.

Vertical upward welding may be used with metal thicker than $\frac{3}{16}$ in [5 mm]; the arc should be as short as possible, with the current 10–15% less than for downhand welding. The electrode should be held at 90° and moved with a slight weave.

After arc or gas welding, all traces of residual slag must be removed from both sides of the joint. Small parts may be immersed and vigorously scrubbed in very hot water; large parts may be scrubbed and rinsed under a stream of hot water. Assemblies involving enclosures or crevices where flux may be trapped may be cleaned by immersion for about 10 minutes in a 5% solution of nitric acid maintained at 60–80°C, followed by thorough rinsing. Unless welds are thoroughly cleaned, flux corrosion will occur, and any flux trapped in a weld (due to excessive

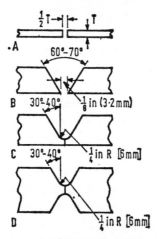

Fig. 47. Preparation of Aluminium Joint Edges for Down-hand Arc Welding.

A: Up to $\frac{1}{4}$ in [6 mm] thick copper back-up bar needed. B: Over $\frac{1}{4}$ in [6 mm] thick. C: Over $\frac{1}{2}$ in [12 mm] thick.

application or agitation of the molten metal) will gradually work to the surface and cause corrosion.

Inert Gas Arc Processes (see also page 110)

Welds made with these processes are superior in strength and liquid or pressure tightness to those obtained with either gas or arc welding, and, no flux being required, there is no risk of corrosion after welding. Very high speeds are possible, especially with machine welding, with corresponding reductions in production costs and distortion.

Some factors governing the choice of either the tungsten arc process (TIG) or the metal arc (MIG) process are set out in Table 19. Until the development of fine wire equipment and the appropriate technique for MIG welding, the TIG process was best suited to thin gauge metal, while MIG welding was more appropriate for plate and thick sections. However, with fine wire MIG equipment, this process is suitable for very thin metal; moreover, of the two processes, MIG is easier to use, particularly with regard to work where position welding is required, since welds can be made with almost equal ease in the horizontal, vertical or overhead positions. For general engineering purposes, the properties of the welds, with either process, are roughly similar.

Probably the main factor governing the selection of process is the economic one. For example, although MIG fine wire equipment may be the best process to use for a particular job, many welding shops may already have TIG equipment (which can be readily adapted for welding most types of aluminium) and expenditure on additional MIG equipment may not be justified, especially for short production runs.

In general, however, where considerable production is involved, the cost of the appropriate equipment will be

Application considerations	Normal first choice
Economic factors:	
Minimum first cost of equipment	TIG
Minimum maintenance cost of equipment	TIG
Minimum training time for operators	MIG
Maximum rate of metal deposition	MIG
Maximum welding speed and lack of distortion	MIG
Automatic welding:	
With addition of filler	MIG
Without addition of filler	TIG
Butt joints, thickness up to $\frac{1}{8}$ in [3 mm]	TIG
Butt joints, thickness greater than $\frac{1}{8}$ in [3 mm]	MIG
Fillet welds	MIG

Table 19. Comparison of MIG and TIG Processes for Welding Aluminium. See also B.S. Specs. Nos. 3019 & 3571 (page 110) and No. 4872 (page 113).

well justified and repaid by the faster welding, lower welding costs, reduced distortion, and the high degree of uniformity and quality of the welds obtained.

Another point to consider is that, although there is no limit to the thickness that can be welded by the TIG process, when the thickness exceeds $\frac{1}{4}$ in [6 mm] both economic and practical considerations favour the MIG process.

Resistance Welding

Due to the high electrical and thermal conductivity of the metal, it is necessary to use machines having much higher current capacity than that normally required for steel; low-power machines will not produce satisfactory welds.

Most of the sheet and strip alloys in general use – in particular those of the 'Duralumin' type (HS_{14}, HS_{15}), aluminium-clad alloys (such as HC_{14}, HC_{15}), aluminium-manganese alloys (NS_3), aluminium-magnesium alloys of the NS_6 type and, to a lesser extent, aluminium of commercial purity – can be spot welded satisfactorily with correct welding conditions.

Commercial purity aluminium presents several difficulties from the point of view of machine capacity, and the tendency for the metal to alloy with the copper electrodes necessitates frequent cleaning of the electrode tips. These difficulties are largely overcome with condenser-type machines, which probably offer the best performance of any type when welding high conductivity aluminium.

In general, the high tensile heat-treated alloys show greater consistency of weld strength than the low tensile alloys, though variations in cleaning procedure and machine settings may result in inconsistencies.

The heat-treated alloys usually tend to cracking and porosity more than the non-heat-treated alloys.

Different thicknesses may be welded together, but if there is considerable difference in the thicknesses it may be difficult to obtain a correct distribution of the current density.

Electrode size and pressure, and welding time, must be carefully regulated to avoid undesirable indentation and to ensure correct location of the nugget.

Dissimilar alloys can be joined, but alloys with melting points and electrical properties near together are easiest to weld. Fully heat-treated alloys may be welded together easily, but it is more difficult to weld heat-treated sheet to fully annealed or cold-worked material.

Degreasing and scratch-brushing of the lap surfaces and the electrode contact surfaces is necessary to remove surface oxide immediately before welding.

Aluminium Brazing (Oxy-acetylene)

The temperature at which joints in aluminium components can be made may be considerably reduced, and fusion of the metal avoided, by using a low melting point silicon/aluminium filler wire with a special brazing flux, a process known as aluminium brazing. The procedure is mainly applicable to fillet and lap joints in thin sheet, tube, etc., but it may be used for butt joints in thicker metal. It may be applied to pure aluminium sheet, aluminium manganese and aluminium-manganese-silicon alloys, and alloys containing not more than 2% magnesium.

Joints must fit with some tolerance, and jointing surfaces must be absolutely clean; laps should not exceed $\frac{1}{2}$ in [12 mm], as the brazing metal must completely fill the joint in order to force out all flux.

The technique involves a general heating of the joint (in contrast to the localised heating and melting of fusion welding) with the flame cone 3 in [75 mm] or more away from the metal; the feed wire with the flux (which melts at the same temperature as the feed wire) is distributed along the joint by a backwards and forwards movement of the flame.

All traces of flux residue must be removed immediately after completing the joint by wire-brushing in boiling water, or with a 5% nitric acid solution if joints are inaccessible to brushing.

British Welding Standards

British Standards for welding processes, equipment etc., listed on the following pages, are obtainable from the British Standards Institution, 101 Pentonville Road, London N1 9ND. Prices vary and a minimum invoice value of £2 applies for posted orders. Price list, reference WELDING SL7, available from BSI on request. Students, educational establishments and BSI members are allowed a substantial discount.

General
BS 499: Welding terms and symbols: Part 1: 1965 Welding, brazing and thermal cutting glossary. Part 2: 1965 Symbols for welding.
Part 3: 1965 Terminology of and abbreviations for fusion weld imperfections as revealed by radiography.
BS 499C: 1965 Chart of British Standard welding symbols.

Safety
BS 679: 1959 Filters for welding.
BS 1542: 1960 Equipment for eye, face and neck protection.
BS 2653: 1955 Protective clothing.
BS 2929: 1957 Safety colours for use in industry.

Processes

BS 693: 1960 Oxy-acetylene welding mild steel.

BS 1140: 1957 Spot welding light assemblies in mild steel.

BS 1723: 1963 Brazing.

BS 1724: 1959 Bronze welding by gas.

BS 1821: 1957 Class I oxy-acetylene welding steel pipelines and pipe assemblies.

BS 2630: 1955 Projection welding low carbon steel sheet and strip.

BS 2633: 1973 Class I arc welding ferritic steel pipework.

BS 2640: 1955 Class II oxy-acetylene welding steel pipelines.

BS 2937: 1957 Seam welding mild steel.

BS 2971: 1977 Class II arc welding steel pipelines etc.

BS 2996: 1958 Projection welding low carbon wrought steel studs, bosses, bolts, nuts and annular rings.

BS 3019: Recommendations for manual TIG welding: Part 1: 1958 Wrought aluminium, aluminium and magnesium alloys. Part 2: 1960 Austenitic stainless and heat-resisting steels.

BS 3571: Recommendations for manual MIG welding: Part 1: 1962 Aluminium and aluminium alloys.

BS 3847: 1965 Mash seam welding mild steel.

BS 4204: 1967 Flash welding steel pipes and tubes.

BS 4515: 1969 Field welding of carbon steel pipelines.

BS 4570: Fusion welding of steel castings: Part 1: 1970 Production, rectification and repair. Part 2 1972 Fabrication welding.

BS 4677: 1971 Class 1 arc welding of austenitic stainless steel pipework.

BS 5135: 1974 Arc welding carbon and carbon manganese steels.

DD 39: 1974 Welding on Steel pipelines under pressure.

Equipment

BS 638: 1966 Arc welding plant and equipment.

BS 807: 1955 Spot welding electrodes.

BS 1389: 1960 Dimensions of hose connections for welding and cutting equipment.

BS 3065: 1965 Resistance welding and heating machines.

BS 3856: 1965 Platens for projection welding machines.

BS 4215: Spot welding electrodes.

BS 4577: Resistance welding electrodes.

BS 4819: 1972 Resistance welding water-cooled transformers (press-package and portable types).

BS 5120: 1975 Rubber hose for gas welding etc.

Consumables

BS 639: 1976 Electrodes for arc welding mild and medium tensile steels.

BS 1453: 1972 Filler rods and wires for gas welding.

BS 1719: Classification, coding and marking of electrodes for arc welding: Part 1: 1969 Classification and coding.

BS 1845: 1977 Filler metals for brazing.

BS 2493: 1971 Low alloy steel arc welding electrodes.

BS 2901: Filler rods and wires for gas-shielded arc welding:

Part 1: 1970 Ferritic steels.

Part 2: 1970 Austenitic stainless steels.

Part 3: 1970 Copper and copper alloys.

Part 4: 1970 Aluminium, aluminium alloys and magnesium alloys.

Part 5: 1970 Nickel and nickel alloys.

BS 2926: 1970 Chromium-nickel austenitic and chromium steel arc welding electrodes.

BS 3067: 1959 Dimensions of blanks for seam welding wheels.

BS 4165: 1971 Electrode wires and fluxes for submerged arc welding carbon and medium tensile steels.

BS 4215: 1967 Spot welding electrodes and electrode holders.

BS 4577: 1970 Materials for resistance welding electrodes and ancillary equipment.

Testing and Inspection

BS 709: 1971 Methods of testing fusion-welded joints and weld metal in steel.

BS 1077: 1963 Fusion-welded joints in copper.

BS 1295: 1959 Tests for training welders. Arc and oxy-acetylene welding mild steel.

BS 2600: Radiographic examination of fusion-welded butt joints in steel, Part 1 and Part 2.

BS 2704: 1966 Calibration blocks and recommendations for their use in ultrasonic flaw detection.

BS 2910: 1973 General recommendations for the radiographic examination of fusion-welded circumferential butt joints in steel pipes.

BS 3451: 1973 Testing fusion welds in aluminium and aluminium alloys.

BS 3923: Methods for ultrasonic examination of welds:
  Part 1: 1968 Manual examination of fusion butt joints in ferritic steels.
  Part 2: 1972 Automatic examination of welded seams.
  Part 3: 1972 Manual examination of nozzle welds.

BS 3971: 1966 Image quality indicators for radiography and recommendations for their use.

BS 4069: 1966 Magnetic flaw detection inks and powders.

BS 4129: 1967 Resistance welding properties of welding primers and weld-through sealers.

BS 4206: 1967 Testing fusion welds in copper and copper alloys.

BS 4397: 1969 Magnetic particle testing of welds.

BS 4416: 1969 Method for penetrant testing of welded or brazed joints.

BS 4870: Approval testing of welding procedures:
   Part 1: 1974 Fusion Welding of Steel.
BS 4871: Approval testing of welders working to approved welding procedures:
   Part 1: 1974 Fusion Welding of Steel.
BS 4872: Approval testing of welders when welding procedure approval not required:
   Part 1: 1972 Fusion Welding of Steel.
   Part 2: 1976 TIG or MIG welding aluminium.

Instruction in Welding and Welding Design

Most aspects of welding technology involved in welding engineering and design are covered by a variety of training courses organised by the Welding Institute and given at their training centre at Abington, near Cambridge, also at courses held periodically at other convenient regional centres. The course programme includes operator training, and special courses for engineer trainees; there are also courses on planning, process control and material behaviour, designed to meet the requirements of supervisory and engineering staff. These are short, intensive courses, and full-time education or training is not available.

The Institute, in collaboration with the British Institute of Non-Destructive Testing, is also responsible for the School of Applied Non-Destructive Testing at Abington. Here operators, technicians, inspectors and technical management staff may receive training in all aspects of non-destructive testing. Practical training is also given in ultrasonics, radiography, and magnetic and dye penetrant inspection.

The above are short intensive courses; full-time education or training is not available at the Institute.

Day and evening classes in welding are, however, usually available at technical colleges in industrial centres. Full time courses of six months duration are also available, to selected applicants, at the various Skill Centres – for full details apply to local employment offices or job centres.

Training in agricultural welding (for farmers and others engaged in agriculture) is available by means of regular classes (usually evenings) arranged by local education authorities; for details apply to the Chief Education Officer at local council offices, or to the County College of Agriculture. Where there appears to be a lack of training facilities, approach the Agricultural Training Board or the local office of the N.F.U. (see telephone directory).

Part 3

Maintenance Welding

Repair work covers a very wide variety of welding applications and the repair welder needs to be a very versatile and adaptable individual to tackle the many different jobs he may be called on to deal with. Broken, cracked or defective castings, ferrous and non-ferrous, form a large proportion of welding repairs, but there are also worn parts to be rebuilt and broken vehicle frames, leaky tanks or pipework to be repaired. Hard facing is another aspect of maintenance that concerns the welder working in quarries and other places where severe wear often necessitates considerable repair welding. The unlimited variety of repair work calls for a wide knowledge of the weldability of metals and of welding methods – often applied under very unfavourable working conditions.

The following notes deal broadly with the main aspects and basic principles of repair welding.

Casting Repairs

The reclamation of broken, worn and faulty castings is one of the most valuable applications of welding, as the replacement of a broken machinery component may involve days, or even weeks, of waiting for a new part, with consequent loss of production – in addition to the cost of obtaining and fitting the replacement. On the other hand, a welded repair may take only a few hours at a negligible cost (compared with that of a new part), possibly even without needing to dismantle the machine.

In foundries, a minor flaw may render a new casting quite useless, the value of the loss being greater if the casting has been machined before the defect is discovered; similarly, machining errors may make an expensive casting unacceptable for the purpose it was intended for. In such cases, welding will enable castings to be reclaimed, eliminating the losses that would otherwise be incurred.

The savings that can be effected by a satisfactory repair are frequently quite considerable, while the cost of the repair may be very little; it is, therefore, worth while studying those factors that influence the success of a welded repair. These factors may be considered in three groups: welding processes, preparation for welding and welding procedure. And the considerations involved apply generally to the welding of any type of casting.

Arc or Acetylene Welding?

With iron castings the choice of welding process is almost entirely dependent on the matter of preheating; undoubtedly the best welds are made on preheated castings, but preheating is expensive, time-consuming and uncomfortable for the welder, and the tendency is to avoid it whenever possible. Welded cold, however, cast iron around the weld point tends to become hard and brittle, and one of the objects of preheating is to reduce this brittleness. Preheating prevents chill hardening and cracking of deposits, and avoids appreciable local expansion at the weld point, which, with complicated castings, might create stress and possible cracking or fracture in other parts of the casting.

With oxy-acetylene fusion welding, preheating is always necessary for all but the simplest castings. The use of bronze welding (by arc or gas) reduces the welding temperature by about 25%, and this reduces the preheating temperature; for simple castings, it may even avoid preheating entirely, since it eliminates melting the casting. This process is excellent for small castings as there is no hardening of the weld junction or the weld metal.

Arc welding is usually employed to avoid preheating, but the repair of cold iron castings by arc welding calls for a considerable degree of skill and patience if good welds are to be secured. Even so, it should be understood that preheating is almost always necessary if high-strength and pressure-tight welds are desired. Pure nickel or nickel/iron electrodes should be used for cold welding, since they provide a weld metal that is ductile and machinable; but even with these electrodes some preheating may be desirable to avoid cracking and hard weld junctions, and, for complicated castings, to reduce the temperature difference between the weld point and the remainder of the casting.

The extremely high and concentrated heat of the arc must be used very carefully in order to avoid local heat build-up and expansion around the weld point. To minimise heat input the weld metal should be deposited in short, thin (stringer) beads with small electrodes and low current. Each bead should be lightly peened to counteract contraction, and the casting should be allowed to cool as much as possible between each run (see also page 124).

Obviously, this procedure cannot be hurried, since success depends on preventing any appreciable temperature rise and expansion in the weld zone; moderate preheat (to take the chill out of the casting) followed by slow cooling will minimise risk of failure in cold weather.

Types of Fracture

If the mechanics of the welded joint are considered, it will be seen that when heat is applied to a fracture the metal expands and any gap between the edges is reduced, or it may close up altogether. When the weld is completed, the heated metal contracts; the deposited metal also contracts into a smaller volume than that into which it was deposited, thus further tending to shorten the overall length across the fracture.

If the fracture edges are the ends of separate free-to-move parts, it is obviously necessary only to separate them sufficiently to allow for expansion, and contraction of the deposit will also be unrestrained. If, however, the fracture edges are not free to move to accommodate the deposit contraction, the weld zone cools in a state of stress, which, with a brittle metal such as cast iron, may be enough to cause fracture immediately or when the part is put into service again.

Fig. 48. Typical Bar-type Fracture.

Repairs usually involve one of three types of fracture. The simplest is the free 'bar' fracture just mentioned and shown in Fig. 48; each part can be separated for the joint to expand and contract. The weld metal in such a joint is restrained only if the weld is very long, in which case lengthways contraction of the weld metal will be resisted by the joining edges and this may cause weld cracking.

The second type of fracture is the same as above except for its location in a wheel rim or spoke, machine frame or other part where expansion at the fracture might cause sufficient lengthening of the member to create stress at other points in the casting; contraction at the fracture will also be resisted by the remainder of the casting. For a successful weld of this type, the fracture edges should be prepared and must then be separated before welding to allow for expansion and subsequent weld contraction.

If the casting is fairly springy, the separation may be achieved by packing or jacks at convenient points, as indicated at A in Fig. 49 – avoiding excessive force, which may cause fractures at other points! Another way is to apply heat to expand other parts of the casting in order to open the joint, as shown at B. The points at which heat should be applied should be in line with the fracture point, and the heat must be maintained during welding. After welding, jacks must be released or heated parts allowed to cool so that the welded portion contracts without restraint.

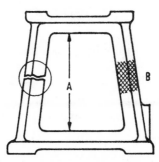

Fig. 49. Typical Frame Fracture.

Even if the break opened when the fracture occurred, it will be desirable to open the break further to allow for weld contraction. Another example of this type of fracture is shown in Fig. 50; here, the break may be opened by jacking at A and/or heating at B, otherwise weld contraction may pull in the rim or, if the rim is stiff enough to resist contraction, the weld may fracture again. For a boss crack, as shown at C, heating at D will open the fracture.

For a rim fracture as shown in Fig. 51, heating at B will open the break; or, for a large, light wheel, heating on a line C–C across the boss may be sufficient.

The third type is where the fracture is entirely sur-

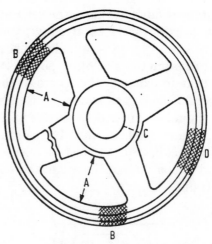

Fig. 50. Fracture in Cast-iron Wheel.

rounded by metal, as in cylinder block cracks, holes in crankcases, cracked pump bodies and so on. In such cases, localised expansion in the weld zone creates a wedge effect, which may extend the crack or convert it into a complete fracture. Total preheating is desirable in order

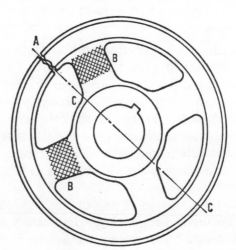

Fig. 51. Rim and Hub Fractures in Cast-iron Wheel.

to lessen this risk, although, using a low-heat input technique, it may be possible to make an arc welding repair with moderate preheating, depending on the rigidity of the casting and the welder's experience and skill. Similarly, an oxy-acetylene bronze weld may be made at black heat, whereas fusion welding would necessitate heating to red heat.

Preparation of Iron Castings for Welding

To attempt a repair on a casting without dismantling it from its associated components is rarely satisfactory, particularly for beginners; accessibility for the preparation of the fracture and control of the welding procedure is most important.

Adequate cleaning of the casting is necessary for the success of most repairs, especially for non-ferrous arc welding and oxy-acetylene bronze welding. Grease and oil may be removed with a degreasing solvent or vapour, or, if solvents are not available, with petrol or paraffin, but only preheating will remove deeply penetrated oil. Corroded areas should be chipped or ground to clean, sound metal.

Cracks may be traced by swabbing with paraffin, or kerosene, afterwards wiping dry and rubbing chalk on the surface to show up any oil retained in the crack. Water-jacket cracks may be traced by lime-washing the suspected area and filling the water space with kerosene mixed with a dye penetrant. Sprayed fluorescent penetrant dyes are also excellent for crack detection. Cracks should be 'stopped' by drilling a small hole about $\frac{1}{8}$ in [3 mm] beyond the visible end of the crack, and for metal over $\frac{1}{8}$ in [3 mm] thick joint edges should be veed to 90° by grinding or chipping, or after preheating (for oxy-acetylene welding) by scraping out with a welding rod. Metal over $\frac{1}{2}$ in [12 mm] thick should be double-veed (if both sides are accessible); welding from both sides minimises heat input and distortion. Gouging electrodes may be used for preparing joints, provided that care is taken to avoid overheating.

For oxy-acetylene bronze welding and all types of arc welding, vees and flat surfaces on thick cast iron can be studded to improve the bond between weld and casting

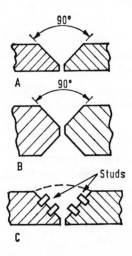

Fig. 52. Preparing Cast-iron Joint Edges for Fusion Welding.

A: Single vee for joints accessible from one side only. B: Double vee for parts that can be turned over and welded from both sides (e.g. the lever in Fig. 44 and spoke welds on wheel repairs). C: Weld surfaces may be studded to improve weld metal bond.

(see Fig. 52, C). This is often done when rebuilding broken gear teeth.

When a part is broken through a machined surface or gear teeth, remachining can be minimised by preparing the joint from the back, leaving a portion of the original fracture unbevelled for lining up.

The various parts of a broken casting should be located and held in position by suitable clamping plates or strips of metal, by bolting to a support or by binding with wire; this must be done before preheating.

When a casting is broken into a number of pieces, it is essential to consider the sequence in which the various welds should be made in order to avoid locked up stresses and distortion. Each weld should be free to expand and

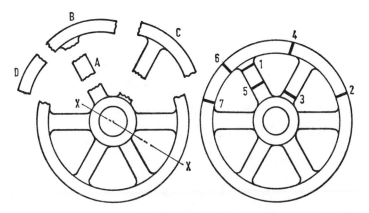

Fig. 53. Typical Welding Sequence for Repairing a Badly Broken Wheel.

First, piece A is welded to B; then piece C is welded to main portion of the wheel. Piece B (with A welded to it) is then welded in place. The wheel is then heated across X–X to open the gap into which D is inserted, and joints 6 and 7 are welded. All welds are allowed to cool slowly protected from cooling draughts.

contract without stressing others parts of the casting, as shown in Fig. 53.

Preheating

Small parts can be preheated with the oxy-acetylene flame; for large castings use propane or gas burners, taking care to heat slowly and uniformly, enclosing the casting – or the portion to be heated – in a brick or sheet-iron furnace built to suit the job.

The furnace wall should be made high enough to allow the casting to be covered with sheet iron or asbestos. The casting should be packed up to allow heat to spread under it, and it should be adequately supported to prevent sagging and distortion. If it will be necessary to move the job during welding, provision should be made for this when the furnace is built.

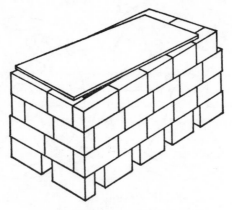

Fig. 54. Typical Temporary Preheat Furnace.
Built of firebrick or sheet iron to suit the job.

Gas flames should be baffled so that the heat does not strike one spot on the casting. Machined surfaces can be protected from the flames by suitable arrangement of the casting or by coating the surfaces with grease and graphite. Cylinder bores can be protected with asbestos discs at the top and bottom of the bore.

Charcoal is one of the best preheating fuels, heating slowly and uniformly; it should be packed around and under the casting. Coke or a blacksmith's fire is not suitable; the heat is too local and the sulphur fumes produced are detrimental to the weld. Charcoal should be used only in a well-ventilated shop as the fumes are dangerous.

For oxy-acetylene welding, preheat to a dark cherry

red; for arc welding or gas bronze welding (if preheating is considered necessary), preheat only to 'black hot'.

Cooling
After welding, both furnace and casting should be covered and allowed to cool as slowly as possible. Small castings can be transferred to a box partly filled with lime and covered to protect from draughts and to ensure slow, uniform cooling.

Arc Welding (Low Heat Input Procedure)
Gas welding a preheated casting follows the usual oxyacetylene procedure, but arc welding a cold casting requires patience and an appreciation of the possible effects of applying local heat to the weld point. To weld a veed joint a bead should be deposited on one side of the bottom of the vee and then on the other, joining these two beads before proceeding to complete the joint. Use small electrodes at the lowest satisfactory amperage; deposit stringer beads not more than 3 in [75 mm] long, peen each bead and allow the weld zone to cool between deposits so that it never becomes more than 'hand hot'.

Weld Hardness
If a cold casting is arc welded with ferrous electrodes (i.e. electrodes with a steel core wire), the weld is very likely to be hard and unmachinable, due to carbon absorption from the casting and the chilling effect of the cold casting on the deposit. If nickel alloy electrodes are used, the weld will only be hard if there has been excessive melting of the joint edges; use a technique that ensures the shallowest possible fusion. Even with pure nickel electrodes, there may be some hardness at the joint edges where the casting metal has been chilled.

With oxy-acetylene welding, hard spots may be caused by neglecting to remove oxide during welding or by dipping a cold welding rod into the pool, or the weld may have been chilled by draughts during or after welding.

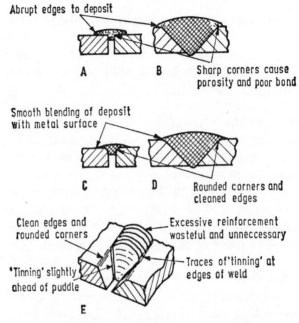

Fig. 55. Preparation of Cast-iron Joint Edges for Oxy-acetylene Bronze Welding.

A & B: Bronze welding faults. C: Square-edge joint; joint surface must be ground or machined clean and corners should be rounded. Useful joint for cast-iron pipes or for any repair joint provided bronze can be left 'as welded'. D & E: Normal 90° vee; top corners should be rounded.

For repairs where hardness is not objectionable or where a large amount of weld metal is required, a ferrous (i.e. mild steel) electrode may be used and will be cheaper than a nickel alloy electrode (the joint surfaces should first be 'buttered' with a nickel alloy electrode). However, the softer and more ductile weld metal deposited by the nickel alloy electrodes is preferable for the complete weld for most repairs and for reclamation work in foundries.

Bronze arc welding electrodes are available for use with ordinary a.c. welding plants and are very useful for small repairs and malleable castings.

In recent years, some special types of cast iron have been developed to improve on the low tensile strength and negligible ductility of the normal iron casting. The weldability of these irons is much the same as that of ordinary grey cast iron; preheating will minimise hardness and porosity, and lessen the likelihood of cracking; nickel alloy electrodes should be used.

Oxy-acetylene welding can also be used for these castings if desired, using cast iron or bronze welding rods. Bronze, or braze, welding avoids any possibility of hardness, and the weld is readily machinable, strong and pressure-tight; it is also cheaper, quicker and, for many repairs, preferable to the fusion welding procedure.

Steel Castings

Parts of earth-moving and quarry machinery, valve bodies, parts of steam and hydraulic equipment, machine frames and similar parts are often steel castings. These are weldable by the arc using the normal steel welding procedure. Any defective metal that might affect the soundness of the weld should be removed. Gas welding is usually not economical for this type of repair owing to the large masses of metal involved, and even for arc welding preheating may be desirable to avoid cracking and porosity due to chilling; stress-relieving reheat after welding is also desirable.

Manganese Steel Castings

Parts subjected to severe impact and abrasion, such as dredge and shovel buckets and teeth, sand and gravel pumps, rock crushers, railway frogs, crossings and switches, conveyor chain parts, and parts of earth-moving equipment and mining machinery, are often manganese steel castings, i.e. steel containing up to 14% manganese. This type of steel is used because it can develop a tough, hard skin under some cold working conditions. The metal can be identified by the fact that it is non-magnetic, and a grinding test will produce a bright bushy spark. As the metal tends to become brittle and crack when heated appreciably, only arc welding can be used. Small electrodes with the low-heat input technique, described on page 124, should be used to avoid the casting becoming more than hand hot during welding. Manganese or stainless steel electrodes should be used, if special electrodes are not available.

Non-ferrous Castings

Magnesium Alloys

Castings not necessitating pressure tightness or high strength, and for use where lightness and/or ease of machining may be required, are usually alloys of aluminium or magnesium, incorporating other elements to give strength or corrosion resistance as may be required. They are used extensively in the automobile and aircraft industries, in shipbuilding, for household equipment and furniture, engine and motor covers, gearboxes, machine frames, brackets and similar parts.

Magnesium alloy castings are much lighter than aluminium and are usually dull grey after being in service, although new castings often have a golden colour due to a chromating treatment. The melting point may be lower than that of aluminium castings, (depending on the alloy) and the metal oxidises more rapidly.

Aircraft castings in both alloys are often heat-treated to obtain extra strength, and welding is not recommended unless a heat-treatable weld metal is used and the part is reheat-treated after welding.

Preheating is generally desirable, but care must be taken not to overheat, owing to the low strength of the metal and the lack of any colour change to indicate temperature. The hot metal may collapse under its own weight before there is an indication that anything is wrong; therefore, castings must be adequately supported so that there is no place where the metal can sag, otherwise a successfully welded job may distort so badly as to be useless. Gas or propane burners, carefully used, are the simplest means for local preheating, but, whenever possible, it is preferable to preheat the entire casting, using air-circulating electric furnaces, particularly if solution heat treatment is required after welding.

Castings must be clean and degreased,* and for inert gas arc welding the oxide skin on each side of the joint must be removed. To avoid overpenetration of the weld metal, steel or copper backing plates may be used, preferably with a groove under the joint. Jobs should be arranged for downhand welding and edges should be tacked.

The use of gas or arc welding is not advisable for magnesium alloys, but if either of these processes are unavoidably employed, care must be taken to remove, by washing, any surplus flux remaining on the metal after welding, taking particular care to wash out places where flux is likely to be trapped. Gas and arc welds will corrode if any trace of flux remains after welding; hence the preference for the use of the inert gas arc process, which not only provides the best quality welds but eliminates any possibility of corrosion arising from flux residue.

For TIG welds on metal over $\frac{1}{8}''$ [3 mm] thick, the joint edges should be bevelled to a 90° vee; over $\frac{1}{2}''$ [12 mm] thick, a double 90° vee should be used.

* See page 121 re degreasing.

Nickel Alloy Castings (Monel, Inconel, etc.)

These castings are used in the chemical, food and other industries where a corrosion-resisting metal is needed. Repairs may be carried out by arc or oxy-acetylene welding, taking into account the general precautions already described. Cleanliness of the casting is particularly necessary because these metals are liable to cracking by sulphur contamination; therefore, any chemical residue, oil, grease, sulphur-cutting oils or paint must be completely removed, and preheating – if required – should be done with propane flames, not oil or coal gas flames or furnaces. In addition, the casting skin must be removed.

For arc welding, electrodes specially designed for these metals should be used. A short arc with medium current is desirable, as high currents may cause excessive spatter; otherwise, the welding procedure is as for mild steel.

A soft, slightly carburising flame should be used for gas welding, and excessive agitation of the molten metal should be avoided to minimise atmospheric oxidation.

Aluminium Bronze Castings

These castings are used for corrosion-resistant service and are best repaired by inert gas arc welding. The metal is 'hot short' and oxidises very readily, and welds tend to be porous. To counteract these difficulties castings should be preheated, ample support should be provided to avoid collapse of hot metal, and atmospheric oxidation should be minimised by avoiding overheating and any unnecessary agitation of the molten metal. Special welding rods and electrodes are available for these alloys.

Rebuilding Worn Parts

The rebuilding of worn parts and the prevention of wear is one of the most interesting and profitable applications of welding, and much time and expense can be saved by rebuilding instead of replacing. Unfortunately, parts are very often kept in service until they are useless due to excessive wear, after which rebuilding is a costly business. A much better and more economical policy is to rebuild before the wear is excessive, thus also maintaining a reasonable standard of operating efficiency. Ordinary mild steel welding electrodes may be used for rebuilding parts on which wear is not excessive but where the rebuilt portion must be machined before the part is used; however, they are not generally suitable for rebuilding parts subjected to heavy wear.

Hard Facing or Anti Wear Welding

The intensity of the abrasion and/or impact that causes wear may vary considerably, depending on the type of work for which the part is used. For example, tram and railway rails and crossings, parts of steel mill, earth-moving, mining and quarrying machinery, and materials-handling equipment are subjected to widely varying types of wear. On the other hand, loss of metal by corrosion and erosion with mechanical abrasion or impact occurs in parts such as steam, chemical and internal combustion engine valves and seatings, pump rods, propeller blades and nozzles, and parts of hot-metal-working machinery. It follows, therefore, that a wide range of rods and electrodes having varying degrees of abrasion and impact resistance has been developed to meet almost every industrial wear-resisting requirement. Arc welding electrodes for this type of welding are often classified as 'hard facing' electrodes, but actually – according to the type of electrode – widely differing degrees of deposit hardness and abrasion resistance are obtainable.

There are two basic types of hard facing electrodes: those that deposit weld metal which is hard as deposited (known as the Martensitic type) and those that give a relatively soft deposit which will surface-harden by cold working (known as the Austenitic type).

Deposits of the martensitic type will not harden appreciably by cold working, but they may be softened by annealing or made harder by quenching. Preheat or post-heat may be necessary in cold weather, or for large masses of metal, to reduce any tendency to crack due to chilling or to minimise excessive hardness of the weld junction. The maximum hardness is usually only obtained by depositing more than one layer (see page 133).

Austenitic work-hardening deposits will withstand considerable impact, since the surface of the deposit hardens as it wears while the metal beneath the surface remains soft and tough, as shown by Table 20.

Brinell hardness of metal as deposited	240
Brinell hardness of deposit *surface* after period of work	500

Table 20. Work-hardening Deposits.

Abrasion-resisting electrodes should be used for sand, gravel and hard-soil handling and working equipment, scrapers, mixers of various types, rollers, etc. Work-hardening deposits should be used for railway crossings and switches, and similar applications.

An extremely hard deposit may be resistant to severe abrasion but may not be able to withstand heavy impact or shock; therefore, where severe abrasion is combined with impact, care should be taken to choose a suitable electrode combining both qualities.

Tubular-type electrodes containing tungsten-carbide

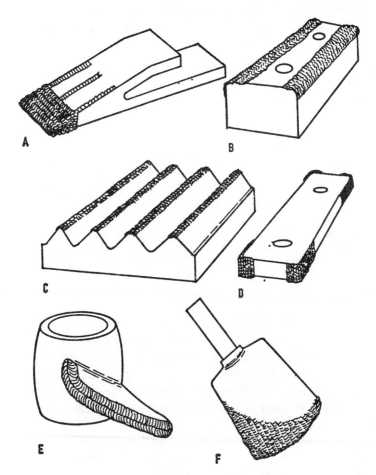

Fig. 56. Typical Hard Facing Applications.

A: All kinds of digging and excavator teeth, bulldozer blades and corners, etc. B: Crusher hammers, breaker bars. C: Crusher jaws, rolls, mantles and cones. D: Pulverisor hammers, shredders, etc. E: Pug mill knives, augers, conveyor spirals, etc. F: All kinds of knives, scrapers, mixing paddles, etc.

granules in various grades are also available and are suitable for soil- and rock-cutting tools, such as well-drilling and coal-cutting bits.

	Hardness of deposit at surface	
	Rockwell C	Brinell
1st layer	29	275
2nd layer	53	524
3rd layer	55	548

Table 21. Hardness of Single and Multi-layer Hard Surfacing.
(See page 139.)

With martensitic hard facings, the deposit hardness depends mainly on the composition of the welding rod or electrode, but it may be influenced by the speed with which the deposit cools and the temperature of the work-piece. Also – as shown above – mixture of the deposit with the melted surface metal reduces its effectiveness, necessitating at least two layers to secure the full value of the electrode. On small parts and oxy-acetylene-welded deposits, there may not be enough quench effect to produce maximum hardness, in which case a hot hard deposit must be used, or the surfaced part must be quenched in water or oil to increase the deposit hardness.

The well-known susceptibility of cast iron to hardening by chilling enables cast iron rods to be used for some oxy-acetylene hard facing applications if the deposit is cooled rapidly, either by depositing onto cold metal or by quenching.

Hard facing electrodes vary considerably in cost and

performance, and usually a trial should be made to ascertain the one most suitable for the job.

Many hard facing electrodes are of the metal powder coating type. These have a very high ratio of metal recovery* and, since they operate at a relatively low arc voltage, there is less dilution of the deposit, which is also smoother and more uniform. The less concentrated fusion at normal amperage gives a wide, flattened bead, which is excellent for surfacing but not so suitable for corners.

Heat-resisting Hard Facings
Ferrous (i.e. iron based) hard facings tend to soften when hot and are not ideal for applications requiring hot hardness. There are, however, non-ferrous hard facings – alloys of tungsten, cobalt and chromium, or high nickel alloys – that have the outstanding advantage of being resistant to heat softening, as well as erosion and corrosion. Such hard facings are suitable for the cutting edges of hot metal working tools and manipulating gear, turbine parts, valves and other parts used for steam, hot gases and oils, and similar applications. These hard facings can, of course, be used for all types of surfacing and are available in a number of grades having different degrees of hardness to suit different types of service; they are available for either oxy-acetylene or arc welding.

Non-welded Hard Facings
There are also hard facing paste alloys that may be applied to a surface or edge and then fused with the oxy-acetylene flame or carbon arc; there is no dilution of the alloy and its maximum wear resistance is preserved.

Powdered metals are also available that can be sprayed with a modified type of oxy-acetylene torch onto a sur-

* I.e. the amount of metal deposited per length of electrode is much greater than that contained in the core wire.

face to build up or provide hardness or corrosion resistance. These surfacings are excellent for cylindrical parts that can be rotated in a lathe in order to obtain an even deposit, up to about 0·060 in [1·5 mm] thick.

Non-ferrous Surfacing

Several non-ferrous metals, chiefly bronzes, are suitable for the non-fusion surfacing of iron and steel parts where a low friction, easily machined and corrosion-resisting surface is required. Deposition is usually done by the oxy-acetylene process, but bronze can also be deposited by arc welding.

		Deposit area				
	mm mm² thickness	50 × 50 2500	50 × 75 3570	75 × 75 5625	100 × 100 10 000	150 × 150 22 500
Kg. of electrodes for four thicknesses of build-up	3	·07	·095	·15	·27	·60
	6	·15	·20	·30	·55	1·2
	9	·22	·30	·45	·85	1·80
	12	·30	·40	·60	1·10	3·60

Table 22. Approximate Weight of Deposit required for Various Thicknesses of Build-up or Hard Facing.

1 kilogram = 2·2 lbs.   3 mm = ⅛ inch (Approx).

See Table 23 for approximate number of electrodes per kilogram of deposit.

Phosphor bronze is used for building up cast iron gear wheels, sprockets and other iron castings; aluminium bronze provides corrosion-resistant and bearing surfaces on steel parts, and is used for the reclamation of bronze marine propellers and for building up worn surfaces on cast iron. Manganese bronze is used for rebuilding worn manganese bronze pump impellers, valves and marine propellers. Nickel bronze will provide wear-resistant surfaces on steel and cast iron valve seats, guides, brake drums, spring shackles, etc. Monel, Inconel and other nickel alloys can be used for the deposition of corrosion-resistant overlays on steel.

Electrode: size length	10 s.w.g. 3·25mm 350 mm	8 s.w.g 4mm 350 mm	6 s.w.g. 5mm 450 mm
Average mild steel electrode	60	45	25
Heavily coated electrode	30	14	9

Table 23. Average Number of Electrodes per Kilogram of Deposit.

Welding Processes

As previously mentioned, arc welding is most generally applied to large parts – mainly because of convenience and speed of application – where it is desirable for the deposit to be hardened by the chill of the depositing surface; or for manganese steel castings, for which the heat input must be kept low. When welding, dilution of the deposit with melted surface metal must be minimised as much as possible; dilution modifies the hardness and wear-resistance of single-layer deposits, and the deposit characteristics of the electrodes are often only fully obtainable with two layers (see pages 134 and 139).

Gas welding has some application for cast iron repairs, non-ferrous surfacing and deposits that need to be hammer forged for smoothing and shaping while hot; also for building up and hard facing small parts to fairly low tolerance with the minimum of grinding after welding. One well-established application is for the surfacing of steam, petrol and diesel engine valve seatings to resist hot gas corrosion. Remarkably smooth deposits are obtained by rotating the valve or seating at a constant speed throughout the operation.

For work on large steel parts, the submerged arc or 'open arc'* processes with automatic feed from a coiled welding wire give the fastest and most economical operation; these are much used for rebuilding worn caterpillar-type track links, rollers and idlers, and also for hard facing bucket edges, crushing hammers, etc.

Preparation for Rebuilding
Rust, scale, paint and grease must be removed, and surfaces corroded by heat or worn by severe impact should be carefully inspected for cracks or other defects, which must be removed by machining, grinding or chipping, or, on steel castings, by flame or arc gouging (gouging should not be used on iron castings). If this preparation will reduce the strength of the part excessively, surfacing should not be attempted, as weld deposits will not eliminate underlying defects and the welding heat is liable to extend any cracks.

Sharp internal corners should be avoided on machined or undercut surfaces, as they weaken the part and tend to create gas pockets in the deposit.

* Wires for open arc welding incorporate the flux.

If the build-up requires more than two layers of weld metal, it is usually uneconomical and undesirable to rebuild entirely with hard facing metal, since thick deposits may crack or spall off. Such parts should be built up to within ⅛ in [3 mm] to $\frac{3}{16}$ in [5 mm] of the required contour with a high tensile or tough steel deposit and finished with hard facing metal.

Depositing surfaces should be flat, and it may be necessary to manipulate a job during welding to maintain an approximately horizontal surface; shafts, rollers, rings, pipes and other cylindrical parts should be rotated. Good handling arrangements make for neater, faster, easier and more economical welding; manipulators, and templates or gauges to show the final shape and thickness of the deposit, should be used whenever possible.

For knives, punches, shear blades and crusher hammers, where the deposit will be subjected to impact, the surfacing metal must have ample support, avoiding overhanging edges. Sharp edges should be removed from external corners, otherwise these tend to overheat. If sharp edges or corners are required in the hard facing, the part must be machined or ground to a sharp corner after depositing, the preparation ensuring a reasonable thickness of deposit under the final machined surface. On cutting edges of ploughs, scraper blades and similar earthworking parts, the deposit should protect the blade surface from abrasion but allow the cutting edge to wear so that it is always sharp.

Hard facing deposits are usually detrimentally affected by too much heat or excessive agitation; therefore, any tendency to deep melt the basic metal or to overheat should be avoided (see page 143 and Fig. 57). In the interests of both economy and efficiency, hard facings should be deposited as smoothly as possible, since grinding removes useful and expensive metal.

Weld metal can often be controlled, and machining or

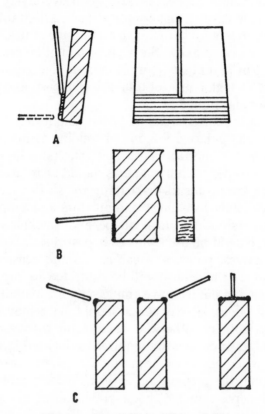

Fig. 57. Hard-facing Procedure.

A: Deep melting of the base metal, and therefore dilution of the hard facing, may be minimised if the surface to be hard faced is arranged more or less vertically. Using the electrode at the angle shown, most of the heat is directed onto the previous run of weld metal; the broken lines show the angle of the electrode for depositing the first bead. B: If the surface is narrow, modify the electrode angle as shown and cover the surface by weaving. C: When it is desirable to preserve the corners of narrow edges, lay a stringer bead on each corner and weave in the deposit between the beads.

other finishing minimised, by using carbon or copper rods, plates and blocks. Plough points, harrow and excavator teeth, star drills, disc edges, well-drilling bits, gear teeth, and many other tools and parts can be built up against suitably arranged shaped copper plates, so that metal can be deposited quickly and very little shaping is required after welding.

Preheating

Preheating is almost always desirable in cold weather, particularly for castings; without preheating, the deposit may be excessively hardened and cracked by deposition onto cold metal; even slight preheating is beneficial. Arc deposits on simple castings may be made with little pre-heating, provided that a low heat input technique is used, but complicated iron castings, comprising thick and thin parts, should be preheated for either gas or arc welding. Steel parts need not be more than black hot, but iron castings should be dull red.

Protection from draughts during welding and cooling, reheating after welding to distribute stresses uniformly, and slow cooling are all important points and should not be neglected.

Distortion

Surface deposits contract during cooling, and on thin parts this may cause considerable distortion, as shown in Fig. 58. On heavy parts resistance to contraction may

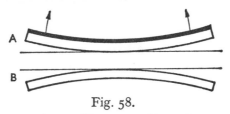

Fig. 58.

Deposit contraction will cause distortion as shown by arrows (A); blades should be preset before surfacing (B).

cause the deposit to crack, but such cracks are not usually detrimental. Welding procedure should, however, be planned to balance these contraction effects. On cylindrical items, such as shafts, rollers, rings and rims of wheels, weld deposits should be made alternately on opposite sides (see Fig. 58); flexible parts should be preset before depositing, so that contraction brings the surface flat again as it cools. Heavy parts may have to be preheated.

Gas Welding

The forward welding method should be used for normal deposits. To avoid deep melting and excessive intermixing of deposit and base metals, the sweat-surface shallow-fusion technique should be used for rebuilding or hard facing steels; the flame for this technique is adjusted so that there is a distinct excess of acetylene, as shown in

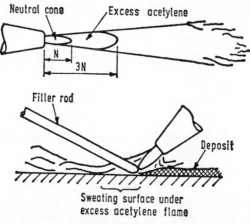

Fig. 59. The Carbonising Flame Surface Fusion Technique. N=maximum length of white core without fuzziness or flicker.

Fig. 59. With this type of flame, the excess carbon in the flame is absorbed by the heated surface, thus creating a microscopically thin, high carbon, low melting point surface layer. This surface melting can be seen (through goggles) as a sweating or glazed area under the excess acetylene flame.

As soon as this condition is reached, the welding rod is introduced between the end of the cone and the metal surface, and depositing proceeds by flowing the deposit over the sweating surface, which is maintained in front of the depositing point.

Arc Welding

Large surfaces may be covered by weaving rather than by laying down overlapping beads side by side. Use large electrodes with small or medium beads in preference to heavy runs; in this way the metal is more easily controlled and a smoother finish is obtained. Narrow edges should be covered by weaving between corner beads.

Deep melting may be minimised by using a medium-to-long arc with low current, by avoiding excessive manipulation, by maintaining a fairly thick puddle and by directing most of the heat onto the weld metal. Electrodes that deposit a flat top bead minimise dilution and tend to give an overall smoother surface with less overlap, thus saving time and heat input. Large surfaces should be covered by using a skip procedure to distribute the heat input as uniformly as possible. On multi-layer deposits on large surfaces, each layer should be deposited at right-angles to the beads of the previous layer.

On worn manganese steel parts, the deposition of an intermediate or 'butter' layer of stainless steel before depositing the hard surface is good practice and minimises deposit dilution, but many hard facing electrodes are suitable for direct deposition on to new manganese steel.

Rebuilding Iron Castings

To build up worn cast iron parts the casting must be treated as for ordinary fracture repairs, otherwise the application of local heat will cause cracking. Hard facing as such is not usually satisfactory, but surfaces may be built up with ferrous electrodes, using a skip technique with narrow beads and ample cooling periods. The deposit is liable to be hard, due to carbon pick-up and chilling by the cold casting.

Manganese Steel Castings

Railway crossings and parts of excavating, earth-moving, dredging and rock-crushing machinery are often manganese steel castings. This metal is very susceptible to cracking if appreciably heated; therefore, the workpiece must be kept as cool as possible during welding. Vees should be prepared by grinding, not by flame gouging, and castings must not be preheated.

Only arc welding can be used, with high manganese steel electrodes, minimising heat input by using the lowest possible current (for the electrode size) and a short arc. A skip technique, allowing the metal to cool between beads, distributes the heat, and the casting should never become hotter than can be comfortably borne by the hand about 6 in [150 mm] from the weld. Fractures should be veed and welded with austenitic stainless steel electrodes,* finishing off the surface of the weld with a layer or two of manganese steel.

Aluminium Bronze Castings

This metal, used for gear wheels and parts needing high strength and corrosion resistance, requires care in welding as it is hot short, oxidises readily and tends to become porous when melted. Preheating is essential to minimise porosity and eliminate the slag that forms readily.

Worn parts may be rebuilt by arc welding in all thicknesses normally encountered by the repair welder;

---

* Special stainless electrodes are available for this application; manufacturers' lists should be consulted.

gas-shielded metal arc welding produces high-quality welds.

Special Surfacing and Rebuilding Applications

Worn Shafts

High-speed power transmission shafts, or crank shafts, are usually made of a high tensile type of steel that is liable to hardening and cracking under welding condi-

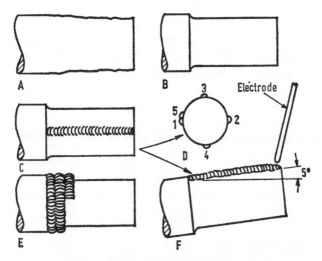

Fig. 60. Rebuilding Worn Shafts.

A: Worn shaft. B: Worn portion machined to remove irregularities and defective metal. Note radius to end of machine portion. C: Building up worn portion with longitudinal beads. D: Method of spacing beads to balance deposit contraction. E: Alternative method of rebuilding with spiral bead. F: Slight inclination of any worn surface helps control of build-up beads.

tions. The physical characteristics of the metal are altered and the fatigue strength of the shaft may be seriously reduced, and there are cases of built-up shafts failing after very short service. Therefore, unless the dynamic stresses are known to be low, the welding of this type of shaft is not recommended.

Satisfactory welding repairs may be applied to mild steel low-speed or stationary shafts, and axles that are used to support brackets, wheels and other machine components. The worn surface should be carefully inspected for cracks, which should be machined out before welding. Uneven heating should be avoided, and the parts should be kept as cool as possible to minimise distortion.

If the worn portion is rebuilt with longitudinal beads (i.e. parallel to the centre line of the shaft), the beads should be spaced round the shaft so that the contraction of each bead is balanced by the contraction of an opposite bead (see D, Fig. 60). Alternatively, the build-up may be achieved by making circumferential beads, taking care to stagger the starting point of each bead so as to avoid a continuous line of starts and finishes. Special care should be taken to ensure good weld deposits, free from notches or defects which may cause failure under stress.

Case-hardened Parts

Generally, the rebuilding of parts that have been case-hardened is inadvisable; however, where it is particularly necessary to rebuild such parts, the component should be softened and the carburised layer machined off. The surface should be carefully inspected for cracks, preheated and rebuilt by oxy-acetylene welding, using a high carbon welding rod. Finally, the part should be cooled slowly, inspected again and then, if necessary, recarburised.

Badly Worn Parts

In cases of excessive wear it is often best to weld on pieces of plate or bar, or (in the case of shafts) even to cut off the worn part and weld on a new piece. A medium carbon or high tensile steel should be used, and pieces of flat spring steel have proved highly satisfactory for re-building worn bucket edges and teeth, etc.

For earth-moving and excavating machinery teeth, specially prepared replacement tips are often available for renewing the worn part, as shown in Fig. 61.[1] In the case of worn track-driving sprockets, service shops will

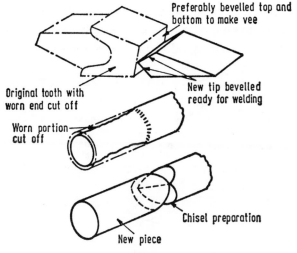

Preferably bevelled top and bottom to make vee

Original tooth with worn end cut off

New tip bevelled ready for welding

Worn portion cut off

Chisel preparation

New piece

Fig. 61.

Badly worn components are often better renewed by welding on new part.

often remove the entire rim, by cutting through the spokes and welding on a new rim. Accurate preparation and positioning is secured by careful jigging, and a planned welding sequence minimises distortion. The abutting ends of the spokes are double bevelled, and the weld runs are staggered from spoke to spoke to minimise heat input at any one point. The welds are lightly hammered while hot to compress the deposit and reduce contraction

[1] Use a stainless steel type of electrode for tip welding.

stresses. One side of the vee is welded on all spokes, after which the wheel is turned over and the opposite side completed.

Reinforcing Worn or Corroded Structures

Outdoor structures are often weakened by rust or corrosion, which reduces the metal thickness, necessitating reinforcement by patching or the application of stiffeners. Many old road and railway bridges need both repairing where they have been subjected to considerable erosion and strengthening to carry heavier traffic than that for which they were originally designed.

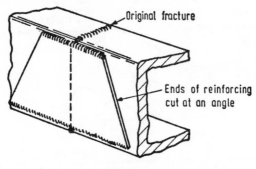

Original fracture

Ends of reinforcing cut at an angle

Fig. 62.

Any reinforcement applied over a repaired fracture (e.g. in a vehicle chassis member) should be tapered at the ends.

Plate girder structures, involving a web joined to flanges by riveted angles, often suffer badly from corrosion of the web plate immediately above the angles; if unchecked, this may eventually separate the web from the flanges. One repair method is to fit a patch plate over the corroded web plate on both sides, making the patch large enough to overlap the angles and to reach sound metal in the web plate at the welds. The patch plates are welded with vertical fillets to the web, and with horizontal fillets to the top and bottom angles.

Where reinforcing plates are applied to strengthen or repair a structure or weldment, the ends of the reinforcement should not finish abruptly but should be cut at an angle to ensure a gradual change in stiffness over the affected area. Mere stiffening with reinforcing plates, without consideration of the position, type and shape of the reinforcement, and of the service involved, may even lead to premature failure by increasing the weight of the structure excessively and changing its behaviour. This is particularly the case with riveted structures, which are usually flexible, and the application of welded-on patches converts them into rigid structures.

In the application of patches or reinforcement work to plate structures, it should be appreciated that, although intermittent welds may provide all the strength required, they are bad practice where corrosion by weather, smoke or fumes is likely to be involved. They are also inadvisable for dynamically-loaded weldments, due to stress concentrations and possible fatigue failures which may occur at the ends of the welds.

Repairs to Sheet Metals

The repair of cracks and the patching of sheet metal items follows generally the procedures already dealt with in Part 2. Edge cracks should be welded outwards toward the edge, preparing, tacking and clamping the joint edges as for a manufactured joint. The repair of long cracks and the welding in of patches usually necessitates skip welding or back stepping in order to distribute the heat and minimise distortion. Patches should be round or oval, or, if they must be rectangular, the corners should be well rounded.

Tacking and clamping to preserve edge alignment, and cooling of the metal at the sides of the joint to prevent buckling should be used as much as possible.

Cracks, fractures and patches in mild steel and stainless steel parts may be very effectively repaired by bronze welding, especially as the lower temperature at which this process is carried out reduces distortion. For stainless steels, a high nickel bronze and an active bronze welding flux must be used, and only the minimum of weld metal should be deposited. The very high nickel bronzes deposit a 'white' weld metal, which is a close match to the appearance of the stainless steel. A soft, slightly oxidising flame should be used to minimise loss of zinc and porosity in the weld.

Underwater Welding

Ordinary arc welding has been used under water (i.e. 'wet' welding) for many years, but the limitations of this process and of the diving conditions under which the welding is carried out have meant that such welds have usually not been rated as anything more than first-aid or emergency repairs. With underwater engineering as it is today – particularly in connection with oil rig and pipeline work – the need to be able to tackle almost any type of underwater repair, and at the same time produce completely reliable first class welds became a matter of highly specialised technical development. For example, working conditions for the welder/diver have been greatly improved and the quality of welding revolutionised by a procedure known as HydroWeld.* In this procedure a transparent open-based box – called a HydroBox – is sealed on to the pipe, or other part to be repaired, completely covering the weld zone. From the bottom of the box upward the box is therefore practically airtight, allowing inert gas to be pumped in to displace the water until the weld point is clear of water. The welder then works through the bottom of the box doing his welding in the dry and in an inert atmosphere. MIG welding is

* Developed and patented by Sub Ocean Services Ltd.

used; the welding controls and the progress of the work are under complete supervision from the surface via closed circuit television and first class welds can be assured in water up to 36 m deep. The work to be done is examined beforehand, also by closed circuit TV; surface scale, rust or marine growth is cleared away by compressed air needle guns, and a working plan drawn up to which the welder works in cooperation with his surface colleague.

It has always been found best to train experienced welders to use diving equipment rather than train divers to weld. D.c. is always employed using motor- or engine-driven generating sets capable of giving 300 to 500 amps.

For cutting steel under water the oxy arc or oxy hydrogen processes are used, depending on the kind of cut required; oxy hydrogen gives a clean edged cut whereas the oxy arc produces a rougher 'cut' more suitable to demolition work.

Part 4

Flame and Arc Cutting

A book on welding would be incomplete without a description of the various flame- and arc-cutting processes that may be employed for cutting and shaping steel plate and preparing castings for welding, and for dismantling steel and iron structures.

The most commonly used process, flame cutting, is basically dependent on the fact that red-hot steel will oxidise, or burn, in an atmosphere of pure oxygen; i.e. if a small portion of a steel plate is heated to redness, a jet of pure oxygen directed on that spot will pierce a hole, or if the jet is moved, produce a cut.

Flame-cutting torches are therefore arranged to provide both a heating flame and a pure oxygen cutting jet.

The function of the heating flame is, of course, to heat the steel where the cut is to be started to red heat; the oxygen jet is then turned on and the torch moved in the required direction, producing a kerf, or cut, the oxidised metal, or slag, falling away from the underside of the cut. The most commonly used cutting nozzles (oxy-acetylene) are in one piece and have a ring of holes surrounding a central single hole. The ring of holes is fed with a mixture of oxygen and a fuel gas, and provides the heating flame; the central hole is the cutting jet and is supplied with pure oxygen only. The heating flame can be adjusted by regulating oxygen and fuel gas valves on the torch, while the pure oxygen jet is controlled by a separate valve. This, on a manual cutting torch, is usually operated by a thumb lever; on machine torches, it may be remote controlled.

Some types of nozzles are in two parts: an inner and

an outer. The heating flame gases issue from the space between the inner and outer nozzles, the inner nozzle having a single hole for the cutting jet (Fig. 63 A, D and E, page 157).

Propane and acetylene are suitable fuel gases for either manual or machine cutting, and give approximately similar results as far as cutting speed and heating times on clean plate are concerned. Propane nozzles usually consist of an inner (brass) and outer (copper) arranged so that the inner is slightly shorter than the outer; the inner is also usually splined on the end where it fits into the outer nozzle, (Fig. 63, D). Another very useful nozzle (oxy-acetylene) is the sheet metal nozzle having one pre-heat jet only. This is for steel plate up to $\frac{1}{8}$ in [3 mm] thick, producing a very clean, distortion-free cut (Fig. 63, B).

Types of Steel

Only a microscopically thin layer of metal at the sides of the kerf (i.e. at the back of the cut edge) is raised momentarily to a high temperature by the heat of combustion of the steel in the kerf, and (if the steel has not been pre-heated) it is cooled rapidly by the cold metal adjacent to the cut.

All normal mild steels (i.e. steels with less than 0·3% carbon) can be cut without difficulty, and there is no detrimental effect on the cut edge. With steels containing more carbon than this, hardening and cracking of the cut edge may occur if the metal is cut cold, due to the quench effect of the cold metal. Preheating may therefore be necessary in such cases in order to reduce the quench effect, and slow cooling after cutting may also be desirable.

Manganese and nickel steels can be cut without difficulty, and without any detrimental or hardening effect on the cut edge. Non-ferrous metals cannot be cut satisfactorily with normal flame-cutting equipment because, unlike the oxide of iron, which melts at a lower temperature than the melting point of steel, the oxides of nonferrous alloys usually have a higher melting point than the metals they are formed from. One of the arc processes or powder cutting must be used in order to increase the temperature and secure a more highly concentrated local heat. Stainless steel cannot be cut with normal flame-cutting procedures, but good results are obtained with arc or powder cutting.

Machine Cutting

Manually-operated torches may be used for any type of flame cutting, but for fabrication purposes mechanised cutting is desirable; the torch is held rigidly and moved steadily at a uniform speed, producing a smooth, accurately cut edge that needs no further preparation for welding.

The cut may be straight or circular, or the direction can be changed whenever required for producing irregular shapes, or the torch can be angled to produce bevel cuts.

Most flame cutting consists of straight line cuts for preparing mild steel plate with either square or bevel edges ready for welding; for this purpose, the torch is usually mounted on a machine which either travels on a specially prepared track or runs directly on the surface of the plate. Machines intended for cutting irregular shapes are usually made to cut the required shape by tracing from a template or drawing. The most advanced machines of this type utilise electronic tracing devices which follow the lines on specially prepared drawings, thus making considerable savings by eliminating templates; drawings are also more easily stored than any kind of template. Since the process may be used to cut up to 40 in (1016 mm) or more thick, there is no difficulty in preparing any thickness of plate likely to be used for welding.

Accurate cutting of plates edges is very important for

automatic welding, for the whole economy of the welding process can be lost if gaps, vees and nosings vary in any way.

Uniformity in depth of nose is particularly important, as a blow-through due to the high penetrative qualities of the arc on an inadequate nose can be very expensive to recover, if, indeed, it does not mean scrapping the whole job.

Electromagnetically-operated gas control valves, power-operated adjustments and automatic torch-height control devices are, therefore, features that increase the productivity and accuracy of cutting machines, and they are of great assistance to the machine operator, particularly where more than one torch is being used.

As previously mentioned, the function of the heating flame is to preheat the point where cutting is to be started; once cutting begins, the amount of heat evolved by the combustion of the steel is far greater than that provided by the flame, but the flame is maintained to keep the slag fluid and to make up for heat losses. Some cutting machines are, however, fitted with a device that automatically reduces the flame when cutting begins, thus reducing the overall oxygen consumption.

An interesting cost-reducing development in mechanised flame cutting is the use of special high-speed nozzles through which the cutting oxygen flows at supersonic speeds, producing a very narrow kerf which reduces the amount of metal lost and is said to enable the cutting speed to be increased 30 to 50% over that obtained with normal nozzles.

In addition to the standard types of machines that are available for the range of general fabricating work, special machines are frequently built to meet the needs of shipbuilding and other industries where specialised applications of flame cutting are often required.

Plate thickness		Nozzle size		Oxygen pressure		Cutting rate	
in	mm	in	mm	lbf/in²	bar	in/min	mm/min
$\frac{1}{4}$	6	$\frac{1}{32}$	0.8	25/30	1·72/2·07	75/80	1905/2032
$\frac{1}{2}$	12	$\frac{3}{64}$	1·2	30/35	2·07/2·41	60/65	1524/1651
$\frac{3}{4}$	20	$\frac{3}{64}$	1·2	35/40	2·41/2·76	55/60	1397/1524
1	25	$\frac{1}{16}$	1·6	35/40	2·41/2·76	45/50	1143/1270
$1\frac{1}{2}$	38	$\frac{1}{16}$	1·6	40/50	2·76/3·45	40/45	1016/1143
2	50	$\frac{1}{16}$	1·6	45/60	3·10/4·14	35/40	889/1016
3	75	$\frac{1}{16}$	1·6	50/65	3·45/4·48	30/35	762/889
4	100	$\frac{5}{64}$	2	50/60	3·45/4·14	24/30	610/762
5	125	$\frac{5}{64}$	2	55/70	3·79/4·82	20/26	508/660
6	150	$\frac{5}{64}$ or $\frac{3}{32}$	2 or 2·5	60/80	4·14/5·51	18/24	457/610

Table 24. Machine Flame Cutting – Square Edge* Oxy-acetylene or Oxy-propane.

* Speeds will be less for bevel edge cutting. Nozzle sizes will be the same for hand cutting but pressures should be higher.

Machines are also available for cutting and bevelling pipe ends, for cutting holes in large pipes, tanks or pressure vessels for welding in branches, or for making special pipe fittings or segmented bends.

Powder Cutting
This is a development of the normal flame-cutting procedure, in which an iron-rich powder is injected into the cutting oxygen stream; the combustion of the powder provides extra heat which will liquify high melting point oxide films. It has been applied successfully to stainless steels, copper, brass and aluminium bronze, but is now superseded by plasma cutting.

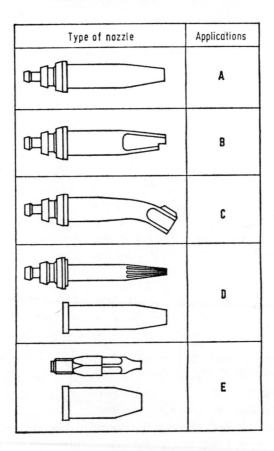

Type of nozzle	Applications
	A
	B
	C
	D
	E

Fig. 63. Cutting Nozzles (Tips).

A: One-piece copper nozzle; the fuel gas and oxygen mix in the nozzle and a ring of preheating jets surround the centre oxygen cutting jet. Available in various sizes of oxygen jet, e.g. $\frac{1}{32}$ in [0.8 mm], $\frac{3}{64}$ in [1.2 mm], etc. For oxy-acetylene only and suitable for all normal cutting work. Will cut in any direction. B: Specially designed for cutting sheet steel up to $\frac{1}{8}$ in [3 mm] thick; must be used so that the oxygen jet is preceded by the single pre-heating jet, ensuring the minimum of distortion. C: For gouging, i.e. for removing defects in welds or on the surface of rolled billets or slabs; also for

Plasma Cutting

This development in arc metal cutting, not mentioned in the earlier editions of this book, is now firmly established for cutting not only ordinary steels but stainless steels, aluminium, copper and other non-ferrous metals quickly accurately and cleanly. In Plasma Arc Cutting, the arc is struck within a nozzle through which gas also passes; the gas constricts the arc and becomes ionised (that is made electrically conductive). Gas and arc emerge from the nozzle at a very high density, temperature, and velocity, so that metal beneath the nozzle is almost instantly melted and blown away. Argon, nitrogen or hydrogen may be used as the carrier gas, but equipment has been developed for using simply compressed air.

The equipment is expensive but since the cutting speed is at least three times faster – assuming reasonable utilisation – the cost per unit length of cut is much lower than with oxy/flame cutting. Using currents up to about 1000 A all metals from $\frac{1}{8}$ in to 7 in thick can be cut, and the cut edge is immediately ready for welding or other methods of jointing. The process is not limited to shop use; mobile units can be employed for taking the cutter to the workpiece.

Fumes and noise tend to be considerable, and with the original equipment relatively low quality cuts were usu-

---

preparing joints for welding, or for removing unwanted welds. For oxy-acetylene only. D: Two-piece nozzle (copper outer, brass inner) for oxy-propane; as above, gases mix in nozzle. The inner nozzle is slightly shorter than the outer and the mixed preheating gases issue from splines cut on the outside of the inner nozzle. E: Old-style short two-piece nozzles for injector-type oxy-acetylene cutters. The preheating gases mix in the torch and issue from the annular space between the inner and outer nozzles.

ally obtained on plate under 1 in thick. However, a recent development provides for water injection to the nozzle to further constrict the arc jet, making it hotter and better defined; water leaving the nozzle cools the work surface, resulting in very much smoother and cleaner cuts. Other advantages are that the life of the nozzle is increased; straight nitrogen can be used instead of other more costly gases, and the noise and fume level is reduced.

Flame Gouging

This application of the normal oxy-acetylene hand-cutting procedure is used to make U-shaped grooves in steel plate, forgings and steel castings, but not stainless steels. It is necessary to use special gouging nozzles (see Fig. 63, C, page 157); by varying the size of the nozzle and by manipulating the torch, the depth and the width of the groove can be varied.

The process can be used for preparing plate edges for welding, or for removing old welds or the root of a weld in preparation for a back run. It can also be used for removing weld or casting defects, unwanted metal or surplus metal from forgings.

As with flame cutting, mild steels can be flame gouged without special precautions, but preheating is desirable for high carbon or air-hardening steels to prevent the formation of a hard zone beside the groove and to avoid any tendency to cracking, although mild hardening without any tendency to crack will be softened by any subsequent welding operation.

Gouging cold iron castings may cause cracking; manganese castings may be gouged so long as appreciable heating of the casting is avoided, otherwise cracking may occur.

Air/Carbon Arc Cutting and Gouging

In this process the metal is melted by arc heat and the molten metal blown away by a stream of compressed air. The carbon electrode is held in a special adjustable holder, which also provides the air jets, and usually the electrodes are copper-coated to increase their life, to ensure good electrical contact and to reduce radiated heat.

The process may be used for preparing welding edges and back-gouging for a sealing run, and for the removal of old welds, surface defects or old hard surfacing deposits. The depth of the groove depends on the size of electrode, the current used and the speed of travel; normally, the operator varies or adjusts the size of groove by varying the travel speed, which is usually between 16 in [406 mm] and 24 in [610 mm] per minute. The width of groove varies from $\frac{3}{8}$ in [10 mm] to $\frac{1}{2}$ in [12 mm] and may be from $\frac{3}{32}$ in [2·5 mm] to $\frac{3}{16}$ in [5 mm] deep.

The current required for normal weld preparation work is between 250 and 400 A, depending on the size of electrode. Although preferably used with d.c., good results are obtainable with a.c. equipment, which is increasingly being used.

Since this is not an oxidation process, its use is not limited to mild steel but is applicable to stainless and heat-resisting steels; it is also used instead of chipping and grinding on iron, steel and bronze castings. As with flame cutting, its use on cold, high carbon steels and cast iron may be limited by possible hardening and cracking due to the rapid chilling of the heated zone by the cold metal and the compressed air.

Carburisation may also occur when the process is applied to austenitic stainless and heat-resisting steels necessitating grinding to remove the carburised skin.

Arc Cutting and Gouging

By employing special electrodes, all metals, including cast iron and stainless steel, can be cut, gouged or pierced using only normal Arc welding equipment. Upwards of 175 A is usually needed, the requirement varying according to the make and size of electrode. For grooving, the electrode is held at a very small angle to the work surface and the molten metal slag is pushed in front of the electrode; by making a series of passes, deep grooves can be cut. The groove is perfectly clean and, on mild steel, requires no futher preparation for subsequent welding.

Stack Cutting

This consists of machine cutting a number of thin plates stacked together in a pack and tightly clamped to ensure that there is no air gap anywhere. The cut is made exactly as though the pack were a solid block; plates as thin as 20 gauge [1 mm] can be cut cleanly with sharp edges and without buckling. Where thin shapes are required, this is the best way to flame cut them with a high rate of production; in fact, for small quantities and large shapes, this method may be more economical than stamping or pressing since there is no die cost.

Cutting Cast Iron

Cast iron can be cut with the oxy-acetylene torch, but since the metal does not oxidise as readily as mild steel it is not possible to produce a neat, narrow kerf. Cutting consists of heating the metal to almost melting point, then opening the cutting oxygen valve and blowing out the hot metal; this procedure is repeated until the cut is completed. The heating flame should be adjusted to have an excess of acetylene.

The cut will be wider than on mild steel; in fact, on

thick metal the torch should be zig-zagged along the line of cut (as shown in Fig. 64) to produce the wide kerf necessary to get rid of the burnt metal and slag to enable the flame heat to reach the lower part of the section.

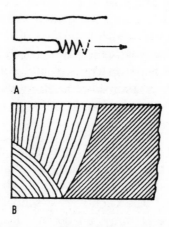

Fig. 64. Cutting Cast Iron.

A: On thick material zig-zagging the cut widens the kerf, and allows the slag and waste metal to fall away freely. B: The starting of a cut on thick material may be simplified by first cutting away the lower portion of the line of cut, thus enabling the cut to be started on relatively thin section.

The cut will be wider than on mild steel; in fact, on thick metal the torch should be zig-zagged along the line of cut (as shown in Fig. 64) to produce the wide kerf necessary to get rid of the burnt metal and slag to enable the flame heat to reach the lower part of the section.

Part 5

Weld and Cut Efficiently and Safely!

1. *Safety in Arc Welding*

(a) Electric shock can cause injury and death; welding machines must be properly earthed; gloves do not protect from shock as, even when working indoors, they may be damp from perspiration. It is dangerous to stand on damp ground when welding.

(b) Makeshift repairs to welding plant may be dangerous; repairs or alterations should be handled by a qualified electrician.

(c) Arc rays are dangerous to the eyes and may cause painful skin burns; therefore, defective helmets, face-shields and lenses should be renewed without delay. Helpers should also wear headshields or goggles with protective glass (see also 7).

(d) White walls reflect arc flash, which may cause inconvenience or discomfort to other workers. Welders should avoid striking an arc if other workers, without eye protection, are nearby. A clear-glass handscreen or goggles should be used to protect eyes when chipping slag.

(e) Do not allow onlookers to watch welding without protective goggles or handshields.

(f) Welding cable and electrode holders must be maintained in good condition. The cable should not lie on work or floor where it can be burnt, pinched or frayed by rubbing on sharp edges, or where it may be a hazard to other workers. Connections must be tight to prevent arcing and to ensure efficient welding.

2. Care of Torches

(a) Stored carelessly, tips are likely to become burred and choked with dirt. Proper boxes or racks should be used.

(b) Using a torch as a lever or hammer loosens joints and may cause gas leaks. Proper spanners should be used (not pliers) for changing tips which should be tightened only enough to ensure a gas-tight joint.

(c) Use proper cleaners for clearing gas holes; if cleaners are not available, a wood splinter or copper wire may be used. Steel welding wire, drills or reamers should *not* be used as they may enlarge the hole, increasing its gas consumption.

(d) If torches become choked, they may be cleared by applying an oxygen hose to the tip and blowing out (with gas control valves open and hoses detached).

(e) Should a backfire occur, gas valves should be closed at once and a few seconds allowed to elapse before relighting. Backfires may be caused by dirty nozzles, nozzle holes enlarged, insufficient gas pressure, hose clogged with acetone or hose too long.

(f) Accumulations of oxide or slag on the end of a tip distort the flame and lower the torch efficiency.

(g) If a tip becomes overheated, it should be cooled by plunging the torch into water with the acetylene turned off but with a little oxygen flowing.

3. Pressure Regulators

(a) Gases must not be used from high pressure cylinders without fitting a pressure regulator; pressure gauges and pressure regulators should be handled carefully if they are to remain accurate and reliable.

(b) The pressure-adjusting screw should be slackened off when shutting down or detaching regulator from cylinder.

(c) Any dust plug, or cap, on the inlet connection should be replaced when the regulator is not in use.

(d) Do not 'make do' with faulty or damaged regulators; have them repaired or reconditioned.

4. *Gas Cylinders*

(a) Oxygen cylinders contain gas at high pressure (approx. 2500 lbf/in^2 [175 bar]*); therefore, they should he handled reasonably carefully. It is dangerous to strike an arc on them or to use them as supports for cutting or welding jobs. They should be stored and used away from heat, and not under machines or shafting, or on oily floors where oil can foul the valves. They should be used upright and attached to a wall, bench or other support so that they cannot be accidentally overturned (see also 9(f)).

(b) See that the valve connection is clean and undamaged before attaching regulator; to clear dirt or liquid, open and close valve quickly. If thread is damaged, the cylinder should not be used.

(c) When regulators are attached, the cylinder valve should be opened slowly; always shut cylinder valve when cylinder is empty or not in use.

(d) *Do not use oil, grease or any lubricant on oxygen cylinder valves, threads or connections, and do not handle with greasy gloves.*

5. *Compressed Fuel Gases*

The maximum discharge rate for an acetylene cylinder should not exceed about 10% of its full capacity. When the discharge rate exceeds this, there is a tendency for the acetone (with which the porous filling inside the cylinder is soaked) to be drawn out of the cylinder with the gas. This causes loss of acetone, reduces the flame temperature and may foul the gas tubing and passages in the regulator and torch. There is no similar risk with propane cylinders, but if the discharge rate is too high the liquid fuel may

* See note on page 16.

not vaporise fast enough to feed the appliance being used. Therefore, with either gas, if the discharge rate is likely to be high – as with large heating torches, thick cutting and similar applications – and in cold weather, it is advisable to couple together two or more cylinders. Always connect full cylinders at the same time, i.e. never couple a full cylinder with one which is nearly empty. Always store and use acetylene and propane cylinders upright.

6. *Gas Hose*

(a) Leaks mean risk of fires and explosions, especially in closed spaces; therefore, keep hose joints tight and hose in good condition; renew if damaged, old or perished. Damaged or burnt sections of good hose should be cut out and rejoined with a proper splicer.

(b) Black or blue hose should be used for oxygen and red for acetylene, and colours should *never* be changed.

(c) Use flash back arrestors on torch inlets and attach hoses with proper clips or ferrules (hose suppliers will do this); wire and unsuitable clips may cut hose. Make sure hose is clean internally before attaching.

(d) Long hoses reduce gas pressure at the torch and are a hazard to other workers; hose lying across gangways should be protected. Hose should never lie in contact with flame or hot metal, or where it may be cut on sharp edges.

7. *Goggles and Headshields*

(a) Goggles and headshields should give proper eye protection, have ample ventilation and fit comfortably; several shades of coloured lenses* are available (see page 173).

(b) Clear glass or plastic lenses must be used over the coloured lenses; replace when they become spotted or broken. Do not weld with cracked, holed or broken coloured lens.

*Plastic (clear and tinted) lenses resist spatter much better than glass.

(c) Onlookers and helpers should wear protective goggles or use headshields when watching welding.

8. *Welding or Cutting Tanks, Drums, etc.*

(a) This work is liable to be highly dangerous unless adequate precautions are taken. If possible, the previous contents of the tank should be ascertained, but if not known they should be treated as inflammable or explosive.

(b) Before starting to weld or cut, the operator or other responsible person should make sure that the tank is empty; even when empty of liquid, residue is often trapped in corners or joints, or on the walls of the tank, and this, when mixed with air, may produce a highly explosive vapour liable to be exploded by a spark or flame; therefore, the tank should be cleaned out thoroughly to remove residue.

(c) Cleaning out with water or compressed air will *not* remove oil or spirit residues or vapour, although washing with strong caustic soda solution will remove heavy oils. The only safe and certain way of cleaning out residue and vapours is to blow through with live steam until the tank is well heated.

(d) In addition, it is often possible to position a container so that it can be filled with water to within half an inch or so of the point where welding or cutting is to be done. This reduces the volume of any explosive vapour, but the space should be ventilated by removing any plugs filler caps and taps that are above water level.

(e) Small containers may be cleaned of residual liquid or vapour by half-filling with *boiling* water three times; allow to stand for about ten minutes, then scavenge with high pressure air to remove any residue.

(f) Pressure vessels, boilers, etc., must be welded under qualified supervision and tested hydraulically or by other approved and supervised methods.

9. *Welding and Cutting inside Tanks and other Confined Spaces*

(a) The foregoing cleaning and safety precautions should be observed. Even if the tank residues are not dangerous, smoke and fumes produced by welding or cutting inside a confined space may be lethal and must be removed by an extraction fan. Failing this, the operator should wear an approved type of breathing mask.

(b) Oxygen must *not* be used to supply fresh air; only air blowers or compressed air are safe.

(c) Hoses and connections of any gas equipment taken inside a tank must be pressure-tight and leakproof, and the insulation of welding cables must be in perfect condition (see also 6(d) and 10(h)).

(d) Do not wear oily or greasy clothing or overalls, or footwear; perferably overalls should be fireproofed. Trouser cuffs should be turned down.

(e) A helper must *always* be on duty outside a tank to watch the operator for signs of fatigue. The operator should wear a harness with a rope attached, which the helper should hold.

(f) Gas cylinders must *not* be taken into a tank or confined space; remove torches and hose from the tank when stopping work even temporarily and certainly when work is finished.

(g) Do not hang unlighted torches inside a tank or near openings.

10. *General Safety*

(a) Oxy-acetylene cutting over wood floors or near locations where inflammable materials are stored can be dangerous; cutting sparks can fly to a considerable distance and will also roll along a floor.

(b) Cutting and welding flames, and the electric arc, are a hazard in rooms containing inflammable materials, gases, liquids or paint. For safety's sake, remove either the inflammable material to a safe place or the job to another location where there will be no possibility of starting a fire or causing an explosion.

(c) Welding areas should be well ventilated to get rid of smoke and welding fumes. Charcoal fumes from a pre-heating furnace in a badly ventilated shop are dangerous.

(d) Fumes resulting from welding or cutting galvanised metal, brass, nickel alloys and stainless steel are unpleasant and injurious, and such work must be done in ventilated situations, or the operator should wear a respirator, drive the fumes away with a fan or use a suction hose near the work point.

(e) An approved type of fire extinguisher, *in operating condition*, should be available at the site of any welding or cutting operations.

(f) Jacketed containers, e.g. hollow castings and similar jobs, should be vented before welding or cutting.

(g) When repairs are carried out 'in situ', make sure that heat will not be transmitted to, and damage, other parts of the machine or installation.

(h) Test for acetylene and oxygen leaks with soapy water only.

(j) Adequate safety precautions should be taken when working off the ground or on staging. The area below should be roped off so that other workers and passers-by will not be injured by falling equipment, sparks, hot pieces of metal or electrode stubs.

(k) Do not use oxygen for dusting off trousers or overalls.

(l) Wear gloves to protect hands, arms and sleeves from heat and sparks when welding and cutting. Wear leggings or spats to protect feet, footwear, and trouser bottoms from sparks when cutting.

Appendix One

Other sources of information relative to welding are the specialised leaflets (usually free) available from the manufacturers and suppliers of welding equipment, electrodes etc. Various other publications are also available, as follows:

HM Stationery Office usually has publications of interest to operators and employers engaged in welding and cutting operations. Apply to Atlantic House, Holborn Viaduct, London EC1B 1BN for details.

The Engineering Industry Training Board offers an advisory service relating to the training of welders and other operatives; details are given in a range of publications, training programmes and manuals. List available from their Publications Department, PO Box 176, 54 Clarendon Road, Watford, WD1 1LB.

Literature covering various aspects of safety and health is available from the British Safety Council, Chancellors Road, London W6 9RS, but only to members of the Council. Membership is, however, open to any individual or employer – apply to the above address.

Welding and Metal Fabrication is published ten times a year by IPC Science and Technology Press, Westbury House, Bury Street, Guildford, Surrey, GU2 5AW. Feature articles, technical surveys, works' reports, equipment reviews and various technology data sheets are available, covering all aspects of metal fabrication.

Metal Construction, the journal of the Welding Institute, Abington Hall, Abington, Cambridge, CB1 6AL disseminates information about metal fabrication, and offers comprehensive data on all aspects of welding applications, including design, and the training of personnel.

The publications of the British Standards Institute are listed on pages 109 to 112.

Sources of information on special metals

Aluminium and aluminium alloys:
Aluminium Federation,
Broadway House,
Five Ways,
Birmingham B15 1TN.

Magnesium alloys:
Magnesium Industry Council,
Address as above.

Copper and copper alloys:
Copper Development Association,
Orchard House,
Mutton Lane,
Potters Bar,
Herts, EN6 3AP.

Nickel and nickel alloys:
Henry Wiggin and Company Limited,
Holmer Road,
Hereford, HR4 9SL

Stainless alloy and high speed and tool steels:
Firth Vickers Special Steels Limited,
Weedon Street,
Sheffield S9 2SU.

Zinc, lead:
Zinc, Lead Development Associations,
34 Berkeley Square,
London W1X 6AJ.

Appendix Two

Possible causes of Weld Defects in Manual Arc Mild Steel Welding

Defect	*Possible cause*
A. Poor appearance	1. Current too high or too low. 2. Erratic manipulation of electrode. 3. Faulty electrode – may be damp.
B. Undercutting	1. Current too high. 2. Electrode held at wrong angle. 3. Travelling too fast.
C. Excessive spatter	1. Current too high. 2. Arc too long. 3. Faulty or damp electrode.
D. Porosity	1. Travelling too fast. 2. Current too low. 3. Arc too long. 4. Impurities in base metal. 5. Unsuitable or damp electrodes.*
E. Cracking	1. Wrong type of electrode (deposit hardening?). 2. Rigid joint (restraining weld contraction).* 3. Bead too concave. 4. Deposit cooling too fast. 3 *and* 4 *above* – travel slower, preheat or protect from cooling influence.
F. Excessive distortion	1. Excessive amount of weld metal (poor edge preparation and fit-up?).

      2. Overheating (current too high or travelling too slowly).
      3. Weld sequence incorrect.

G. Brittle welds   1. Unsuitable electrodes.*
      2. Deposit is hardening (wrong electrode?).
      3. Excessive base metal pick-up (use shallow penetration technique).

H. Slag difficult   1. Current too high.
   to remove   2. Electrode damp.

I. Difficult   1. Electrode damp.
   striking   2. End of electrode covered with slag.†
      3. Poor earth.
      4. Voltage/amperage too low.

* Use low hydrogen electrode.
† Happens with low hydrogen electrodes.

RECOMMENDED SHADES OF TINTED FILTERS FOR ARC AND GAS WELDING AND CUTTING

Arc Welding (Head or Handshield lens)		Gas welding (Goggle lens)	
Amps	Shade	Operation	Shade
up to 100	EW 9	Welding aluminium oxy cutting	G 3
150 to 250	EW 10 or 11	Sheet steel and copper welding Silver soldering	G 4
300 to 400	EW 12 or 13	General fusion welding Rebuilding and hard facing	G 5
over 400	EW 14	Heavy fusion welding	G 6

Appendix Three

Metrication: SI (Système Internationale) Units

Common units recommended by the Welding Institute:

Electrode stickout (for MIG welding) – measured to nearest millimetre (mm), e.g.:

$$\tfrac{1}{4} \text{ in} = 6 \text{ mm}; 2 \text{ in} = 50 \text{ mm}.$$

Wire feed speed (or burn-off) – in metres per minute (m/min), e.g.:

$$50 \text{ in/min} = 1\cdot27 \text{ m/min}; 600 \text{ in/min} = 15\cdot24 \text{ m/min}.$$

Welding or cutting speeds – the unit depends on the speed, e.g.:

$$12 \text{ in/min} = 300 \text{ mm/min}; 48 \text{ in/min} = 1\cdot22 \text{ m/min};$$

$$10 \text{ ft/h} = 3 \text{ m/h}.$$

Gaps and root faces – in millimetres, e.g.:

$$\tfrac{1}{32} \text{ in} = 0\cdot8 \text{ mm}$$
$$\tfrac{1}{16} \text{ in} = 1\cdot6 \text{ mm}$$
$$\tfrac{1}{8} \text{ in} = 3\cdot2 \text{ mm}$$
$$\tfrac{3}{16} \text{ in} = 4\cdot8 \text{ mm}$$

Sizes of welds – leg length always in millimetres; **Length of weld** – in millimetres up to 1000 mm (approx. 40 in) then in metres (m).

SYMBOLS FOR CHEMICAL ELEMENTS

Al	Aluminium	Mn	Manganese	S	Sulphur
C	Carbon	Mo	Molybdenum	Si	Silicon
Co	Cobalt	N	Nitrogen	Sn	Tin
Cr	Chromium	Nb	Niobium	Ta	Tantalum
Cu	Copper	Ni	Nickel	Ti	Titanium
H	Hydrogen	O	Oxygen	V	Vanadium
Fe	Iron	P	Phosphorus	W	Tungsten
Mg	Magnesium	Pb	Lead	Zn	Zinc

THICKNESS OR DIAMETER EQUIVALENTS IN
INCHES AND METRES

in	*Exact equivalent* mm	*Practical equivalent* mm
$\frac{1}{16}$	1·59	1·6
$\frac{3}{32}$	2·38	2·5
$\frac{1}{8}$	3·18	3
$\frac{3}{16}$	4·76	5
$\frac{1}{4}$	6·35	6
$\frac{5}{16}$	7·94	8
$\frac{3}{8}$	9·53	10
$\frac{1}{2}$	12·7	12
I	25·4	25

ELECTRODE SIZE EQUIVALENTS

s.w.g.	in	mm
16	$\frac{1}{16}$	1·6
14	$\frac{5}{64}$	2
12	$\frac{3}{32}$	2·5
10	$\frac{1}{8}$	3·25
8	$\frac{5}{32}$	4
6	$\frac{13}{64}$	5
4	$\frac{15}{64}$	6*

* Not a standard Continental size; more usual size is 6·3 mm.

Pound and kilogram equivalents:

> 1 lb = 0·454 kilogram
> 1 kilogram = 2·2 lb
> 5 kilograms = 11 lb (approx.).

NUMBER OF ELECTRODES PER 100 METRES

Total length of electrodes	Equivalent number of electrodes for various lengths		
	Length of each electrode		
	300 mm	350 mm	450 mm
100 metres	328	281	219
250 metres	820	702	547
1000 metres	3280	2810	2190

TOTAL METRES PER 100 ELECTRODES

Electrode length mm	300	350	450
Equiv. metres	30·5	35·3	46

* These are nominal lengths and millimetre sizes quoted are not necessarily exact equivalents of inch sizes.

TEMPERATURE CONVERSION
CELSIUS TO FAHRENHEIT AND VICE VERSA

Degrees Celsius	Degrees Fahrenheit									
	0	10	20	30	40	50	60	70	80	90
0	32	50	68	86	104	122	140	158	176	194
100	212	230	248	266	284	302	320	338	356	374
200	392	410	428	446	464	482	500	518	536	554
300	572	590	608	626	644	662	680	698	716	734
400	752	770	788	806	824	842	860	878	896	914
500	932	950	968	986	1004	1022	1040	1058	1076	1094
600	1112	1130	1148	1166	1184	1202	1220	1238	1256	1274
700	1292	1310	1328	1346	1364	1382	1400	1418	1436	1454
800	1472	1490	1508	1526	1544	1562	1580	1598	1616	1634
900	1652	1670	1688	1706	1724	1742	1750	1778	1796	1814
1000	1832	1850	1868	1886	1904	1922	1940	1958	1976	1994
2000	3632	3650	3668	3686	3704	3722	3740	3758	3776	3794
3000	5432	5450	5468	4486	5504	5522	5540	5558	5576	5594

APPROXIMATE COMPARISONS BETWEEN THREE
METHODS OF ESTABLISHING HARDNESS

Brinell (HB)	Rockwell 'C' (HRC)	Firth or Vickers (HV)
100	—	—
150	—	154
200	15	205
250	24	257
300	31	307
350	37	362
400	43	423
500	51	550
600	58	702
700	66	960

Index